Designed and published by APECS Press.

This edition is limited to four hundred copies.

Copy number

163

DOLAUCOTHI GOLD
A VISION REALISED

Dr Alun Isaac

Contributors to plans, drawings, and photographic images:
Dr Alwyn Annels, Consultant Mining Geologist
Dr Peter Brabham, School of Earth, Ocean
and Planetary Sciences, Cardiff University.

APECS Press
Caerleon

First published in 2012 by APECS Press

*Editing and design by
APECS Press Caerleon*

ISBN 978-0-9563965-1-8 (Hardback)
ISBN 978-0-9563965-2-5 (Paperback)

The publisher gratefully acknowledges the financial support of:

SRK Consulting (UK) Ltd.
School of Engineering, Cardiff University.
School of Earth, Ocean and Planetary Sciences, Cardiff University.

Printed in Wales by
Dinefwr Press, Llandybïe, Carmarthenshire

For Margaret Rose

and

*former colleagues, students and friends
in the National Trust and the
Pumsaint and District community*

ACKNOWLEDGEMENTS

The Dolaucothi Gold Mine project extended over twenty one years and involved several organisations and many individuals. The relationships between people as part of an organisation or community can determine the ultimate success of a cooperative venture. The achievements of the years 1978-1999 are due almost entirely to the warmth of the close interaction between the National Trust, the University at Cardiff and St David's University College, Lampeter, and the community of Pumsaint and District.

Grateful acknowledgement is expressed to the staff of the National Trust for their advice, encouragement and involvement throughout the years of rehabilitation and development of the gold mine lease area. From the prime movers, Hugh Griffith, Peter Mitchell and Emrys Evans in 1978 to Philip James, at the end of the 21-year lease in 1999, the Land Agents and staff of the National Trust ensured that the work of mine recovery and renewed interest progressed safely and efficiently, up to and beyond the present time.

Throughout the time at Dolaucothi, the Vice-Chancellors, senior academic and administrative staff at Cardiff and Lampeter provided the interest, support and resources to enable the staff and students of Engineering, Earth Sciences and Archaeology to develop a facility of great educational benefit. The early vision of a centre for Higher Education was soon enhanced to that of a visitor centre for all ages, covering a wide range of specific and general interests. The staff and students of the Department of Mineral Exploitation, Cardiff University, where the project was first conceived, very much appreciated the opportunities that Dolaucothi offered and the author wishes to express appreciation of such support on behalf of his colleagues and himself.

The community of Pumsaint and District were highly intrigued and often amused by the sight of staff and students working in cold, wet and muddy conditions that were clearly not the University norm. This may have been the reason for their kind and generous support on a daily basis. Warm acknowledgement is expressed to them all for opening their hearts and homes, and in particular to Tegwyn and Iris Williams and family at Dolaucothi Farm, and to the late Tom and Morfydd Cleminson at Dolaucothi Lodge. Their homes became the early centres of accommodation and catering without which the general health and enjoyment would not have been so high.

As ever in projects of this kind, there are those who see beyond the immediate challenges to the possibilities that can be realised by a visionary approach, prodigious energy and creative enterprise. Such is the role of sponsorship and even without vested interests, many supporters were found to enable the financial needs of the project to be met. It is to those sponsors who are listed in the Appendix that sincere gratitude is now expressed; without their support, the project could not have succeeded.

Special acknowledgement is made of the strong bonds developed with colleagues, particularly during the five year rehabilitation period. The contributions of Dr Alwyn Annels, Professor Brian Smart, Professor Keith Williams, Dr Edward Hellewell and postgraduate students in those early years helped to provide the foundations for the subsequent successful development.

Dr Annels, in particular, remained with the project over the twenty-one years involved and I wish to express my warm thanks to him for his personal support throughout, and for the reading of the text prior to publication.

With changes in staffing and priorities, other colleagues emerged in the later years and tribute is paid to Professor Vernon Morgan, former Head of Engineering for his consistent support and in particular, his strong encouragement of the publication of this written record.

Dr Peter Brabham of Earth, Ocean and Planetary Sciences has continued the work of his predecessors to the present, and for his contribution of photographic images and personal notes that have been incorporated into this account, sincere thanks are offered.

As the images in this book show, postgraduate and undergraduate students were at the heart of the changing face of the Dolaucothi Gold Mine. Many of those students are now occupying senior positions in the engineering industry and other professions and almost all retain a strong affection for their time at Dolaucothi. Dr Michael Armitage, Group Chairman and Corporate Consultant (Resource Geology) of SRK Consulting (UK) Ltd is a prime example. However, there are too many others to mention individually, but all are thanked for their personal contributions to a unique project.

The valuable contribution rendered by experienced diamond drillers, particularly Gareth Williams and Fred Mann, is gratefully acknowledged. David Glinn, of the School of Engineering technical staff, also became highly proficient in the use of the Longyear 34 wireline rig and spent many hours at the controls in often inclement weather. These drillers not only provided invaluable experience for our students but also performed miracles in their efforts to keep the aging rigs in operation.

The writers of all written records of this nature need the encouragement, support and approval of those closest to them. In my case, this has certainly been true and although words cannot really express my gratitude to my wife, Margaret Rose, I thank her for her patience and involvement over the years of the project and those following in the compilation of this record.

CONTENTS

APPENDIX

FOREWORD

Given the long history of Dolaucothi the twenty-one years of the Gold Mine Project may be seen as a fleeting moment but to perceive those two decades in those terms would be to ignore just how important the years from 1978 onwards were in placing the site at the forefront of public awareness and consciousness.

Through the productive partnership between various departments in the University at Cardiff, St. David's University College, Lampeter and the National Trust, the importance of Dolaucothi as a place of international historic significance has increased exponentially.

The Dolaucothi Project was the brainchild of Dr Alun Isaac and Dr Alwyn Annels of the Department of Mineral Exploitation in Cardiff University. Certainly they were the prime movers but, as they so readily acknowledge, they were members of a much larger team whose enthusiasm and commitment saw the transformation of the mine site from a Caravan Park to an internationally acclaimed heritage tourist attraction.

It is entirely appropriate that the transition should have been undertaken by engineers and scientists as the winning and production of gold throughout history has required high standards of mining engineering, organisation and hard labour. Those involved in the project had these requisites in abundance. The opening of the abandoned workings and the creation of the Field Centre were inspirational. As indeed, has been the painstaking and detailed historic research and archaeological excavation that has helped us understand how the mining at Dolaucothi evolved. Key to the success of the project was the response and subsequent support of the National Trust. It took vision and energy for all the individuals and organisations to work together.

The core of the project has been to provide intellectual and physical access. From providing 'hands on' training for students, enabling school children to experience the mines and to creating a major tourist attraction – since 1984 over seven hundred and fifty thousand people have visited Dolaucothi.

Today the mines are a well-established and highly regarded visitor attraction and most who take the trip through the tunnels and chambers find the experience enlightening and rewarding. To see the pick marks made by the ancient miners scored into the forbidding rock makes us aware of just what was required to win the precious gold. It gives an opportunity to make a personal connection with our forebears. It is not only the long distant past that is represented at Dolaucothi. Close links between the Department of Mineral Exploitation and the mining company, Rio Tinto Zinc (RTZ), together with the National Trust's expertise in generating financial support, resulted in removal and reconstruction of the surface equipment from the Courtauld-owned Halkyn Mine in north Wales to Dolaucothi. The re-erected head frame and other surface buildings and equipment give so much more context and understanding of 20th century mining operations.

Perhaps the essence of Dolaucothi is the story of human endeavour and it is good to reflect that the desires and ambitions of the past were being employed in the latter years of the last century.

It has been a privilege to write this foreword to pay a small tribute to those who worked so hard, so long and so enthusiastically to realise the vision.

RICHARD KEEN
Heritage, Landscape and Tourism Consultant

(Formerly with the National Museum of
Wales, Cardiff, and the National Trust for Wales)

I

INTRODUCTION

THE FASCINATION OF GOLD

GOLD, the word that has excited the imagination from earliest times – the Phoenicians, the Egyptians, the Greeks, the Romans, the Aztecs and the Incas, the Spaniards and others. The many properties of gold such as its rarity, workability and durability have made a major contribution in the evolution of the human species. However, its colour is perhaps the main property that has fascinated and driven the continuing search for its possession.

This precious metal is usually a lustreless yellow when found in its natural state. It sometimes has a reddish tinge when containing copper as in some Indian gold and can be of a green hue when mixed with silver as in some Canadian gold. It appears white when mixed with platinum, this being a popular choice for wedding rings, and is a rich yellow when containing silver and copper. The gold at Pumsaint, Carmarthenshire, South Wales, hidden under the gently folding hills near the border between South and Mid-Wales, may well have been sprinkled on the plaids of Celtic chieftains. It undoubtedly adorned the purple robes of Roman Emperors.

In the latter part of the twentieth century, and in partnership with the National Trust, the vision and energy of staff and students of the University of Wales, Cardiff at the old Roman goldmine produced an asset of historic and cultural interest. Fieldwork activities at the Dolaucothi Gold Mine, by University staff from both Cardiff and Lampeter between 1970 and 1999, informed and enlivened the experience of their students. In conjunction with the National Trust and the community of Pumsaint and District, these activities aroused the interest of the general public and led to the creation of a prime tourist site. The development of its educational potential helped to enhance the traditional National Trust philosophy that had in general promoted the ethic of conservation, preservation and self-discovery in previous years.

THE INDUSTRIAL REVOLUTION, HIGHER EDUCATION AND A NATIONAL ASSET

The Industrial Revolution of the nineteenth century led to changes in education in much of the developed world. Science and engineering became more strongly linked with new courses, introduced into higher education in order to satisfy the demand for well-qualified engineers. In particular, during the second half of the Twentieth Century, it became generally accepted that blending initial training within the education process, assisted a student's better understanding of the principles involved leading to a more effective entry into industry.

Technological change

The rate of technological development post-1950, with the advent of computers and electronic innovation, demanded even greater emphasis on the quality of an engineer's development. The design and maintenance of increasingly sophisticated machinery and equipment needed to be addressed in order to raise levels of operational efficiency, productivity and health and safety. A skilled labour force that included a high proportion of well-qualified engineers was also needed to meet the changing face of industry and new patterns of operation.

Improved courses

The European mining industry responded by providing new and improved courses at universities and polytechnics in those countries that possessed large numbers of mines. In particular, Britain, France and Germany produced engineers and managers who, not only satisfied national requirements but also those of other countries such as South Africa, North and South America, Canada and Australia.

New technology

New technology also brought about a change in the syllabuses and methods used in higher education. The large-scale, test apparatus previously used in laboratories disappeared, to be replaced by computer-linked, miniaturised versions and by computer modelling. As a result, a greater volume and quality of test results led to better understanding of activities in the mining environment. It also assisted subsequent development of equipment, prior to full-scale trials at manufacturers' test locations and in underground mines.

Collaboration of disciplines

The interaction between the different specialisms that emerged, Mining Geology, Mineral Extraction and Minerals Processing, benefited students during their early education and training. The changes occurring in higher education led to the development of field centres with laboratories and typical mining environments remote from the universities. Cardiff, Strathclyde and Nottingham Universities developed such field centres after 1970, to give greater realism in the education of their students.

Fieldwork

In 1978, the Department of Mineral Exploitation at University College Cardiff commenced the rehabilitation of the old Roman gold mine at Pumsaint, Carmarthenshire, to serve as a field centre for its students. University staff and students accomplished the work of making it safe for fieldwork activities from 1978 to 1984. This occurred together with practical work such as geological mapping, topographic surveying, geochemical and geophysical exploration, environmental monitoring, and minerals processing. The new Field Centre became an educational facility for all years of engineering students with the formation of the School of Engineering in 1988. This continued until 1999, when the National Trust took over the lease of the mine workings. Though the University relinquished control over the lease area at this time, formal courses and visits to the site by students of the School of Earth and Ocean Sciences, Cardiff University continued to take place.

Cardiff University, the National Trust and Sponsorship

The years 1978 to 1984, were the keystone years in the regeneration of the mine – draining flooded zones, clearing ways into collapsed tunnels and shafts, making roof and walls safe, and re-entering old working places. The years 1986 to 1988 continued the development of the mine, particularly with the installation of the 1930s vintage mine surface buildings and equipment from the closed Olwyn Goch Mine at Halkyn in North Wales.

Student education was always a high priority throughout the rehabilitation and development of the gold mine. In later years, an education project was introduced involving Primary school children that provided a springboard for developing in future generations an awareness of Roman engineering and Celtic lifestyle, legend and culture.

The National Trust introduced a programme of public visits during the summer months of 1984, for its members and tourists, following informal trials by University staff from 1981 to 1983, to assess visitor interest in the site. Throughout the years 1978–1999, when Cardiff University held the lease of part of the gold mines complex, the emphasis was always upon education with enjoyment. This approach was extended by the National Trust to embrace the visiting public and the response was always enthusiastic.

This account shows how the vision for the future of the Gold Mines site was successfully achieved by the close co-operation throughout the project between the University, the National Trust and the many sponsors.

II

Mining & Minerals Education at Cardiff, 1891–1991

1891–1935: COMMENCEMENT OF TEACHING

The University College of South Wales and Monmouthshire began mining education in Cardiff in 1891. Over the following century, teaching reflected the changes occurring in world mining. From 1890 to 1920, South Wales enjoyed great economic success, based primarily on its coalmining activity. Although the range of its coal types supplied industry and shipping – steam, coking and anthracite coals – its nature of deposition and geological structure led to high levels of coal dust production and methane emission. William Galloway, a leading mining engineer and consultant, became the first Head of the Department of Mining due to his special interest in the nature and cause of the many explosions occurring from these sources.

The University of Wales established the College in 1883 in Newport Road near the northbound Rhymney Valley railway line (Chrimes, 1983). The Department of Mining housed between 10 to 15 students following degree or diploma courses in mining, in a private house in the Parade, to the rear of Newport Road. In 1907, the College Principal, E. H. Griffiths, summarised the discussions of College and Mining Industry representatives in a report concerned with the setting-up of a major new mining school at Cardiff. For various reasons, this failed to progress and the Coal Owners established the South Wales and Monmouthshire School of Mines at Treforest near Pontypridd in 1913. The School provided Diploma courses there until 1928, during which time, academic links between Treforest and Cardiff led to three or four-year Joint Diploma courses in coalmining.

1935–1968: STAGES IN DEVELOPMENT

T. David Jones's appointment to the Chair in Mining in 1936 resulted from the financial support of the College, the Coal Owners and the Miners' Welfare Fund. His research interest in developing methods of suppressing airborne dust in mines led to the establishment of the South Wales and Monmouthshire Coal Owners Research Association. However, the war years, 1939–1945, interrupted the planned development of the Mining Department that included more space and facilities. Shortly after the appointment of John Sinclair to the Chair of Mining in 1947, a new temporary building provided improved accommodation until 1956. Thereafter, a new, multi-storey, permanent building in The Parade provided purpose-designed lecture rooms and laboratories, it being occupied in stages between 1956 and 1960, with continued sole occupancy until 1991.

Aerial view of the Engineering Faculty layout (centre), with the new Mining Department shown within the central black border. The northbound Rhymney Valley railway line lies immediately adjacent with the Lord Mayor's Mansion shown (top centre) (*c*.1960).

Front view of the Mining Department facing The Parade, as it appeared in 1960; the central elevated walkway was added later with the formation of the School of Engineering in 1988.
The building is presently used by the School of Physics and Astronomy and the School of Computer Science (c.2010).

The post-war period saw some significant developments in the British mining industry with its nationalisation in January 1947. This move provided the political will for major investment with new mines and mechanisation of the underground extraction of coal. Although reconstruction of the mining industry proceeded at pace, the mid-1950s saw the start of rationalisation and contraction of British coalfields and the number of mines, due to a reduction in demand for coal. As a consequence, the Department of Mining experienced severe difficulty in recruiting students in the 1960s that led in 1968 to a College enquiry into its future.

1968–1991: MAJOR EXPANSION AND THE CENTENARY

Following this enquiry, the Department's name was changed from Mining to Mineral Exploitation, reflecting a broader approach to world needs with its increasing demand for metals and minerals of all kinds. With John Platt's appointment to the Chair and Headship of the new Department in 1968, emphasis upon academic flexibility included options in Mining Engineering, Mining

Geology (later to include Exploration Geology) and Minerals Engineering. The success of this approach appeared in a number of ways with new staff appointments, increased student numbers, links with other Earth Science Departments, new research activities and industrial support.

By 1975, the Department's academic staff level had risen to its highest point since its inception in 1891 with two Professors, a Reader and nine lecturers. This allowed co-operation with the Department of Geology in a Joint Honours scheme and with the Departments of Geology and Physics in the development of a degree in Geophysics. Under its new name, renewed interest led to its numbers increasing to around 100 undergraduate students and up to 30 postgraduate students.

As a result of further funding from Government Research Councils and Industry, beneficial interaction occurred between teaching and research in areas such as geotechnical engineering, environmental control, geological exploration and recycling of waste materials.

Academic research between 1969 and 1975 led to the realization of the educational potential of the workings of the abandoned Ogofau gold mine on the Dolaucothi Estate at Pumsaint in Carmarthenshire. This, together with the greater student numbers and the new curriculum content encouraged the development of an off-site facility in 1978, as a field laboratory for the teaching of subjects such as surface geochemical and geophysical exploration, underground geological and geotechnical mapping, mine surveying and environmental studies.

Accordingly, staff and students developed a Mining Field Centre at this disused gold mine, which was originally worked in Roman times, later at the turn of the nineteenth century and finally from 1936 until its abandonment in 1940. The mine lay on what had been the Dolaucothi Estate of the Lloyd-Johnes family at Pumsaint, the estate being donated to the National Trust in the early 1940s. The Department and the National Trust worked in partnership from 1978 onwards in the rehabilitation and development of the old gold mine towards its new status as an educational field centre and visitor attraction.

The Department expanded its overseas mining interests between 1970 and 1991 with undergraduate visits to mining fields in Europe, Canada, Africa, and North America. The research contacts developed in these countries led to funding and postgraduate student recruitment. Departmental staff provided advice and assistance to newly-developing universities in South America, in Peru and the Dominican Republic under the auspices of the Ministry of Overseas Development, London, with these universities wishing to base their mining departments on the Cardiff model.

The period 1968 to 1978, under the headship of Professor John Platt, could well be considered one of the finest in the Department's life, and, at that time, the Department of Mineral Exploitation was regarded by senior University staff as one of the success stories of the College.

However, a government rationalisation survey into the teaching of mining subjects at British universities during the early-1980s resulted in the closure or merger of long-established departments. The subsequent merger of the Departments of Mineral Exploitation and Metallurgy into the Division of Materials and Minerals Engineering resulted from international changes that reduced the mining industry requirement for graduates.

The emergence of the new University of Wales College, Cardiff, in the mid-1980s, resulted from the merger of the two Cardiff Colleges, University College Cardiff (UCC) and the University of Wales Institute of Science and Technology (UWIST). Within this enlarged University, the School of Engineering, formed in 1988, contained five divisions, one being the Division of Mining and Minerals Engineering.

Finally, after 100 years of life, 1891 to 1991, the teaching of mining engineering at Cardiff ceased with its last graduates entering the world mining industry and also many other careers such as mining finance, stock broking, human relations management and engineering consultancy; a far cry from its early beginnings. However, the teaching of mining-related subjects continued until 2002, within the Department of Geology at Cardiff (later renamed the School of Earth Sciences and eventually the School of Earth and Ocean Sciences), via an M.Sc. course in Mineral Resources, until 2002; its undergraduate courses in exploration geology continue at the present time.

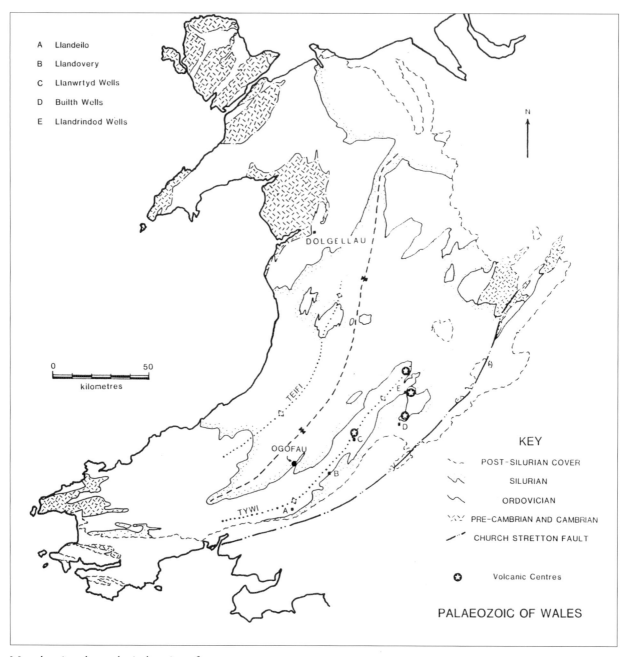

Map showing the geological setting of
the Dolaucothi Gold Mine (Ogofau).

III

DOLAUCOTHI GOLD MINE

(Previously known as Ogofau Gold Mine)

HISTORICAL BACKGROUND

The Welsh name *Ogofau* (meaning caves in English) was generally given to the ancient mine workings near the village of Pumsaint due to the cave-like openings to the workings which revealed evidence of Roman activity (*c.*AD 60-210). Early modern developments occurred from 1872 to 1912 with the final period of mining taking place from 1934 to 1939.

Cave-like entrance to the mine workings (Mitchell Adit) showing bedded rocks that may indicate the presence of gold ore in the crest of the anticlinal structure (*c.*1975).

During the early years of Roman interest in the mine site, water was brought along two aqueducts (one seven miles long and the other, four miles in length) to serve a number of large tank-like excavations overlooking the proposed area of open pit mining. Subsequently, the water was released from the tanks in a planned manner to scour and remove soil from the hillside, to assist in the fire-setting technique of ore extraction, and to clean and separate previously crushed ore. The series of open pits give evidence of this activity that is still clearly visible.

With completion of ore extraction by surface methods, mining continued underground with access by a number of tunnels leading off the main open pit. Artefacts discovered in the 1930s included wooden roof supports, a cradle-shaped ore carrier and a fragment of a water wheel. These objects discovered in an old Roman stope are now held at the National Museum of Wales, Cardiff. Anecdotal information from miners of the last period of mining described one Roman excavation on the 100ft level below ground as *The Cathedral,* due to its large size.

The various stages of modern mining at Dolaucothi may be summarised as shown below.

1871–1872	Eurion Eurglawdd Mining Co.
1872–1875	Private small scale
1888–1897	South Wales Gold Mines Co.
1905–1906	Private – Johnes Family
1906–1909	Ogofau Proprietary Gold Mining Co. Ltd.
1909–1912	Cothy Mines Ltd.
1934–1937	Roman Deep Holdings Co.
1937–1939	British Goldfields (No. 1) Co.

In 1871/72, the mine was worked firstly in a small-scale entrepreneurial manner by the Eurion Eurglawdd Mining Company; however, this quickly failed. From 1872–1885, local small scale operations also resulted in failure. The South Wales Gold Mines Company (1888–1897) commenced operations in 1888 and, with a small work force, developed some adits and a small shaft. Due to the low grade of the ore at 1.5gm gold/tonne, the company eventually went into liquidation.

In 1905, the Johnes Family commenced a further operation with the construction of two adits and an interconnecting internal shaft, (this development became the main part of the lease area secured by the University in 1978). At this time, a small mill for ore crushing was erected in the main open pit, its foundation still evident on site. This venture also failed after one year, due to lack of capital.

The Ogofau Proprietary Gold Mining Company Ltd (1906–1909) operated profitably for a few years, but again, lack of capital prevented simultaneous exploration and extraction of ore reserves, and in 1909, the lease was sold to Cothy Mines Ltd. (1909–1912). This company was responsible for the sinking of a vertical shaft to the 100ft level below the Open Pit where it intersected a thick quartz lode at 90ft depth, thereafter referred to as the Roman Lode. Subsequent assays revealed the presence of gold but extraction was not pursued, and in 1912, heavy water inflow resulted in high pumping costs and closure.

1934 saw the formation of the Roman Deep Holdings Company (1934–1937) who undertook a fairly comprehensive mine development programme consisting of shaft sinking and tunnel drivages. Unfortunately, this work turned out to be poorly planned and organised, resulting in the restriction of longer-term economic mining.

With the transfer of the lease to the British Goldfields (No. 1) Company (1937–1939), gold ore production was substantially increased for over twelve months by a labour force of 165 men. However, in October 1938, financial

View of part of the mine surface showing the shaft headgear and winding engine house. Note the inclined tunnel entrance (centre right) leading to the 100ft level in the mine (*c*.1938).

resources were again exhausted and production ceased. In 1940, following some further exploratory work by diamond drilling, the mine pumps were stopped, the workings allowed to flood, and the mine was declared abandoned. However, the mine area continued to hold interest for those interested in its archaeological significance and its potential as an educational field centre.

Miners in the Roman Lode workings on the 260ft level in the mine (*c.*1938). Note the general absence of roof support, the naked flame carbide lamps, and the headwear.

Group of shaft inspection miners standing outside the cage and underground mineworkers standing inside at commencement of shift (*c*.1938).

Some of the 200 men employed at the mine in 1938 celebrating the refining of the first 100oz (3kg) bar of gold.
(Photo: The National Trust).

Dolaucothi Mansion in its heyday, a beautiful Georgian-style country house. Built in the early 18th century, it was eventually demolished in 1952 due to its serious disrepair.

One of the community events held at Dolaucothi House (*c.*1920–*c.*1930).

Historical records show that the land on which the workings lay had been in the ownership of the Lloyd-Johnes family since the 1600s. With the River Cothi running within its boundaries, the land became known as the Dolaucothi Estate, because of the meadows adjacent to the river ('dolau' is the Welsh for meadows). The National Trust became the owner of the 2,577 acres estate in 1941–1944, it being donated by H. T. C. Lloyd-Johnes, the last surviving member of the family, following a destructive fire at the Mansion in the late 1930s.

Ogofau Mine lost its manpower in 1939 due to poor economics, the problem of shipping concentrate to America or Germany for refining and the military demands of the Second World War. Interestingly, the last mine manager (Nelson, 1944), wrote up notes later published in a mining journal, stating that:

'These notes have been written more or less from memory under active service conditions in Great Britain.'

Nelson's papers provided a very useful source of information for companies who may have been interested in later mining activity. However, the mine lay abandoned and increasingly derelict for the next forty years.

General appearance of the mine surface following its closure and official abandonment in 1939/40. The building foundation seen on the left supported a small mill and machinery for ore crushing.

ARCHAEOLOGICAL DEVELOPMENTS

Serious archaeological interest developed in the 1960s in relation to the Roman period of mining at Ogofau. However, the discovery in the locality of Roman gold ornaments in earlier years, and their donation to the Carmarthen Museum by the Lloyd-Johnes family, stimulated the interest of the Carmarthenshire Antiquarian Society. It was this interest that led to sponsorship of archaeological studies, led by Professor Barry Jones and Dr Peter Lewis of Manchester University, from 1965 to 1975 (Jones and Lewis, 1971; Lewis, 1977). Subsequently, a major archaeological publication by Barry and Helen Burnham, reported the work of staff and students of St David's University College, Lampeter, from 1987 to 1999 (Burnham & Burnham, 2007).

Manchester University staff suggested that although the site may well have been exploited in pre-Roman times, its present shape resulted from the technological knowledge of Roman mining engineers. In particular, their use of aqueducts, running for several miles to holding tanks, enabled them to scour lower-lying hillsides for signs of gold-bearing rocks. The water in these tanks assisted the use of the 'fire-setting' technique, i.e. alternately heating the rock face and then rapidly cooling it with water, this leading to fracturing of the rock. Water would also have been used to separate gold grains from the broken and crushed ore-bearing rock, and further used to transport waste rock to lower dumping points.

The present-day line of the aqueduct (leat) can be clearly seen just over halfway up the hillside. This leat carried water (from right to left) for approximately 4 miles from the River Annell to one of the holding tanks above the mine workings. A similar leat carried water (from left to right) for over seven miles from the River Cothi to the holding tanks (c.2010).

Cross-sectional view across hillside showing a figure standing in the line of the aqueduct (*c.*2010).

View of the breached southern side of one of the holding tanks (this one lies above Mitchell Pit) estimated to have had the capacity of over 5 million litres (100,000 galls) of water (*c.*2010).

The existence of a small fort at Pumsaint is shown on the Ordnance Survey Map of Roman Britain (5th Edition). The Manchester University work provided an initial analysis of Roman activity at the gold mines site. Knowledge of the aqueduct systems supplying the site with water and hydraulic power, the opencast workings and small tunnels, and the associated fort and settlement, was developed further by the twelve year archaeological research activity of the University College Lampeter staff and students. The Burnham publication provides a standard reference source of information on archaeological aspects of the Roman period of occupation.

Archaeological excavations under the direction of Professor Barry Burnham, University College, Lampeter at the Roman fort, Pumsaint. (Photographs courtesy of the Department of Archaeology, University College, Lampeter, c.1991).

THE NATIONAL TRUST

Following acquisition of the Dolaucothi Estate in the early 1940s, the National Trust directed its resources to repairs and renovation of properties and the replanting of woodlands. Limited attention had been paid to the gold mine site, apart from temporary fencing of some of the openings to the underground workings. An increasing emphasis on health and safety in general required further National Trust resources to be devoted to the Estate in the 1960s.

A relatively small additional source of income was generated by leasing the open pit area of the mine site to the Caravan Club of Great Britain. However, movement of the Caravan Club to a larger site nearby was encouraged by the report of some minor ground subsidence together with the dangers inherent in temporarily fenced-off tunnels and shafts. Following previous links with the Department of Mineral Exploitation, the National Trust consulted Professor John Platt, Head of Department, for advice on a permanent solution to the on-site safety of its members and visitors. This coincided with the Department's own search for a suitable location that would allow field-based facilities for all its students.

View from the open pit floor looking down the main vertical shaft showing the rubble and miscellaneous materials that provided a seal at 10m below the concrete capping (c. 1986).

The advice given was to infill a highly inclined, small dimension tunnel that gave access to the 100ft level below ground. This operation was completed in 1976/77 with several thousand tons of limestone rock making a permanent sealing-off. The nearby 140m (480ft) deep vertical shaft also required further infilling having been partially filled with rubble and other miscellaneous materials to a depth of about 10m (33ft) below the shaft's concrete capping. A well-secured man-hole cover completed the safety provision at the shaft.

IV

VISION AND INNOVATION

THE DOLAUCOTHI RESEARCH COMMITTEE

The establishment of the Dolaucothi Research Committee of the National Museum of Wales in 1968, led to detailed investigations of Roman mining activities by the Manchester University staff. However, the links between Cardiff University and the National Trust members on the Committee resulted in geological/geochemical exploration on the hillsides above the gold mine by the Department of Mineral Exploitation staff and students, including Dr Alwyn Annels, Dr Geoffrey Steed and Dr Gordon Kingston, with surveys made of the accessible underground workings by Dr Edward Hellewell. Surveys led by Professor Frederick Pooley, were also made of the gold content in the fine waste rock tailings material in a number of the settling ponds used in the 1930s period of mining.

View of one of the three settling ponds of waste tailings after concentration treatment of the crushed ore (c. 1936–1939).

These investigations provided an understanding of the types of gold mineralization and how it may have occurred. They also stimulated interest in continuing research with the recognition that the site was ideal for the practical training of all students of the Department of Mineral Exploitation.

In 1972, Professor Platt reported to College authorities on the results of work undertaken at the site in the previous two years. His proposals for future development, in particular, the setting-up of a Mining Field Station, were well received. With the departure of the Caravan Club from the site in 1976, the opportunity presented itself for the development of a field centre for practical training. This involved arrangements with the representatives of the College (Gareth Lewis, Solicitor), the National Trust (Hugh Griffith, Agent) and the Crown Estate Commission (Alan Grierson, Agent).

DEPARTMENT OF MINERAL EXPLOITATION

A 21-year licence from the National Trust gave the Department of Mineral Exploitation access to the site and interior of the mine. A lease from the Crown Agent for a corresponding period allowed use of the mine as a base for mining instruction. The period of licence and lease from 1978 to1999 saw the involvement of the Senior District Inspector of Mines for South Wales, Mr Albert Davies (later to become an Honorary Professor of the School of Engineering, PhD (Wales) and an international consultant on health and safety matters). He permitted use of the workings by staff and students on condition that a qualified mining engineer was appointed as Mine Manager and that there was full observance of the appropriate mining legislation. These requirements were satisfied with the appointment of Dr Alun Isaac of the Department staff as Mine Manager, as a result of his professional qualifications and previous managerial experience in the South Wales coalmining industry. To complete the picture, a Management Committee was established from members of the Department staff, to establish operational policy and administrative support, and to generate strategic vision.

The work of the Dolaucothi Research Committee and the Universities of Manchester and Cardiff from 1968 to 1978 aimed to provide knowledge of previous mining activities and facilities for future mining education. The early vision producing these aims broadened in later years with the recognition that the Gold Mine site offered much more as a regional and national asset. In view of its location on the Dolaucothi Estate, the name of the mine was eventually changed from its traditional local name of Ogofau Mine to become the Dolaucothi Gold Mine.

An early visit to the mine by Mr Albert Davies (on right), Principal District Inspector of Mines for South Wales (*c.*1975)(later to become Deputy Chief Inspector of Mines for the UK), together with Dr Alun Isaac, Mine Manager, outside the exit from the top of the mine workings in the lease area (*c.*1977).

This region of West Wales contained several sites of tourist interest, enhanced by the attractive coastline of Cardigan Bay. The mine with its gold and Roman associations added a further attraction for British and overseas visitors. This unique mine also raised awareness of Wales and the Welsh identity, since it was the best preserved and most technically advanced Roman mining site in Britain. Finally, the broader vision also saw the gold mine in its widest sense, with its potential for education and enjoyment in many areas of learning and by all ages.

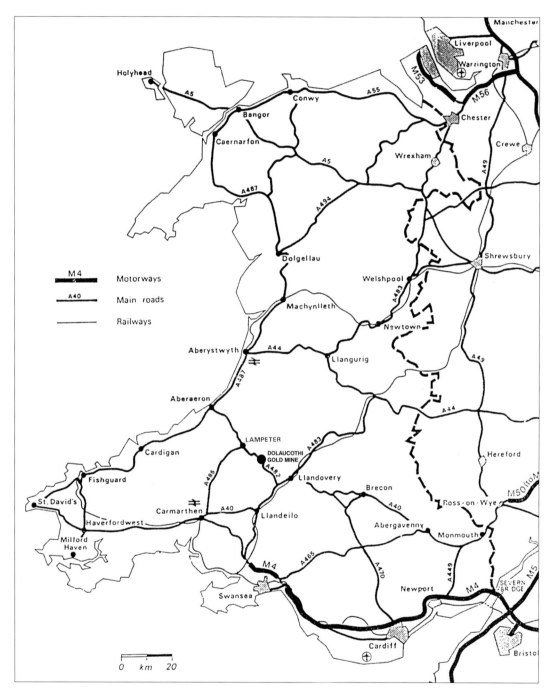

Map showing the location of the
Dolaucothi Gold Mines.

V

PHASE ONE:
REHABILITATION AND EDUCATION
1978–1984

LOCATION AND LAYOUT

The mine workings at Dolaucothi lie approximately 60 miles (120km) to the north-west of Cardiff, near the boundary between South and Mid-Wales. The workings extend for over half a mile (1.1km) in a north-east to south-west direction along the hillside that forms the south-east side of the River Cothi valley (Allt Cwmhennog); the mine is situated adjacent to the main A482 road between Llanwrda and Lampeter near the village of Pumsaint.

The scene facing academic and technical staff of the Mineral Exploitation Department in the early to mid-1970s was that typical of abandoned metalliferous mine workings – a main surface open pit, tunnel entrances partially hidden by overgrown vegetation, collapsed tunnels, flooded zones and open, unguarded shafts.

Unguarded and partially flooded entrance to Long Adit (*c*.1975).

43

Collapsed zone 10m inside the entrance to Long Adit (*c.*1975).

Dr Alwyn Annels (on left) and Dr Alun Isaac at the unguarded entrance to Mill Adit (*c.*1975).

Unfenced top of the 30m deep vertical internal shaft connecting Mitchell and Long Adits (*c.*1975).

Difficult travelling way up an old working place (gold vein on left) from Mitchell Adit to the surface (*c.*1975).

Following a site survey that revealed the extent of the workings, the decision was made to restrict the proposed Field Centre lease area, and hence, legal responsibility, to those parts of the mine that could be made relatively easily accessible with the resources of time, labour and finance then available.

Composite plan view of the 1930s mine workings.

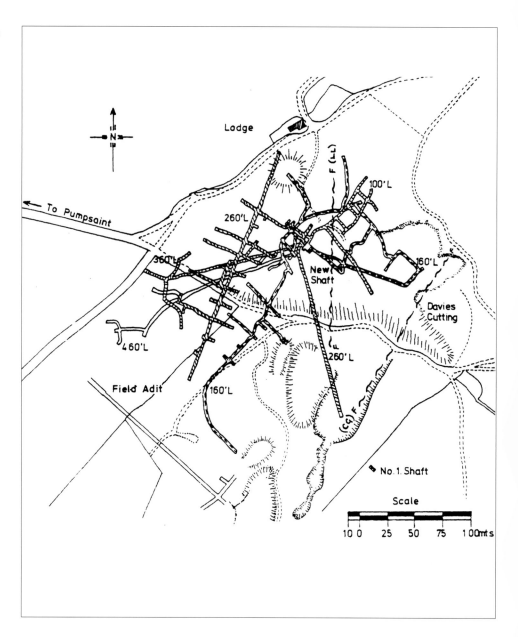

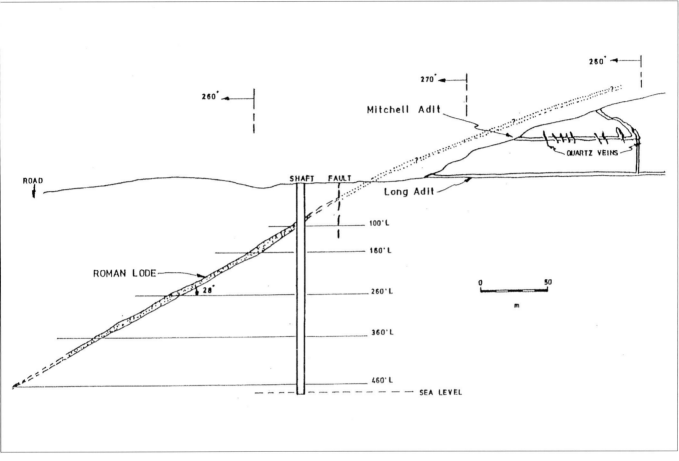

The main area of the mine workings comprised a large open pit that led to an upper hillside section containing three gently inclined tunnels, known as adits, and referred to as Long Adit, Middle Adit and Mitchell Adit. An additional adit referred to as Mill Adit, penetrated directly from the base of the open pit. Below the open pit lay a labyrinth of underground workings, some of which were of Roman origin, with most being from the last period of mining, 1934 to 1939. Previous remedial activity referred to earlier, had closed off entrances to workings below the open pit; they were thus inaccessible due to flooding and were not included in the lease area.

Following discussions between the University, the Crown Estate Commissioner and the National Trust, the lease area was established in 1977, after which initial clearance work commenced in the following year. The drawings shown illustrate the relationship between the different parts of the lease area that were to be the focus of attention between the years 1978 to 1984 for the first phase of the twenty-one year period of the lease.

Longitudinal cross-section of mine, the lease area being that shown on the top right of the drawing above and including Long Adit.

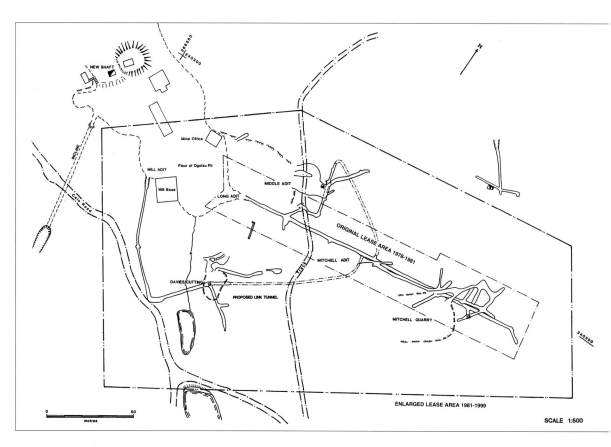

Plan view of the initial lease area (1978–1981) and the longer term enlarged lease area (1981–1999).

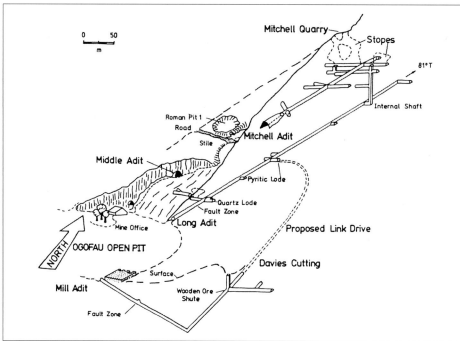

Schematic drawing of the main part of the lease area.

INITIAL ASSESSMENT

University staff visited the mine site on several occasions from 1970 to 1977. The information obtained then enabled an assessment to be made later of the physical requirements needed for the safe re-opening of the proposed lease area of the abandoned mine.

The gently inclined tunnel entries, Long, Mitchell and Mill Adits, were self-draining and self-ventilating, thus requiring no pumps and fans. These were major advantages but it was envisaged that they could only be enjoyed as the work of rehabilitation proceeded in the Phase One period, 1978 to 1984. There-after, mine development would probably require more positive drainage and ventilation facilities using pumps and fans.

The work of rehabilitation of the mine was assessed as requiring safe and secure access, installation of lighting, power, drainage, and debris removal facilities, and the construction of management and operational facilities. In order to accomplish this work, it was recognised that mine rehabilitation activities could provide a valuable opportunity of engaging the Department's students in a number of important aspects of their career education. In addition, a wide range of theoretical studies by undergraduate and postgraduate students could be incorporated simultaneously, as part of their educational development.

RESOURCE ACQUISITION

The resources needed for the establishment of a Mining Field Centre at the gold mine included manpower, time, finance and materials. Based on the recognition that voluntary self-help was essential for the success of the work, staff and students provided the required labour force, supplemented by external engineering specialists.

On this basis, the time available was limited to that of seven-day periods during the Christmas and Easter vacations, and longer fourteen-day periods during the summer vacations. The short vacation field courses needed to have a mix of practical and theoretical activities, in contrast to the Summer Camps that were designed for the practical engineering activity of rehabilitation.

Department staff energetically tackled the vital ingredient of finance with representations made to the University authorities, national and international mining companies, other organisations and private individuals. Recognising the academic and potential recruitment values of such a Field Centre, the University provided an initial grant of £2,500 with further funding made available from the existing general vacation grants system. An initial grant of £2,000 was also donated from an international mining company.

Front cover of the Trust Fund
Appeal booklet (*c.*1979–1981).
(A5, 12 pages).

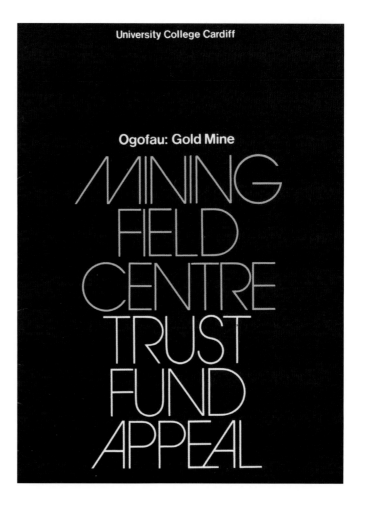

However, the major source of finance obtained was from the setting-up of a
Trust Fund Appeal in 1979 that raised over £12,000 from various benefactors.
This sum was invested with the annual interest being used to increase capital
growth and to provide for revenue expenditure. Together with other funding
provided by the College as part of undergraduate field course activities, this
investment income helped cover the costs of routine maintenance, insurance,
lease, equipment and mine development.

While the initial costs of rehabilitation were covered from the sources described,
the assistance of the South Wales coal industry in providing large quantities of
materials from closed mines made a further indirect financial contribution. The
value of these materials during the course of the work was estimated to exceed
£4,000. The financial assistance of the many organisations and individuals in
the setting up of the Field Centre at the Dolaucothi Gold Mine is gratefully
acknowledged and recorded in Appendix A3.

ORGANISATION OF REHABILITATION ACTIVITY

The record of the rehabilitation work from 1978–1981 given below shows the contribution of the Mining and Minerals Engineering and Mining Geology staff and student groups in the short vacation programmes. Staff and students from all the Department's teaching programmes were involved to some extent in the short vacations and in all the Summer Camps. This approach enjoyed considerable success in encouraging interaction between staff and students during practical activities and also in social situations.

PHASE ONE REHABILITATION ACTIVITY, 1978–1983

July	1978	Summer Camp 1978
December	1978	Part 1 Mining Engineering Field Course
April	1979	Part 2 Mining Engineering Field Course
May	1979	Part 2 Mining Geology Field course
July	1979	Summer Camp 1979
December	1979	Part 1 Mining Engineering Field Course
April	1980	Part 2 Mining Engineering Field Course
September	1980	Summer Camp 1980
December	1980	Part 1 Mining Engineering Field Course
April	1981	Part 2 Mining Engineering Field Course
July	1981	Summer Camp 1981
December	1981	Part 1 Mining Engineering Field Course
March	1982	Part 2 Mining Engineering Field Course
July	1982	Summer Camp 1982
September	1983	Part 1 Mining Engineering Field Course

The personnel involved during the first three years of the rehabilitation is given in the table below. However, an estimate of those involved for the years 1978-1984 would amount to 2,500 staff/student days.

Course	Participants		No. Days	No. Personnel Days
	Staff	Students		
1978				
Summer Camp (July)	2	8	12	120
Mining Engineering Part 1 (Dec.)	3	21	7	168
1979				
Mining Engineering Part 2 (April)	2	22	7	168
Mining Geology Part 2 (May)	1	6	4	28
Summer Camp (July)	2	8	12	120
Mining Engineering Part 1 (Dec.)	2	15	7	119
1980				
Mining Engineering Part 2 (April)	4	21	7	175
Mining Geology Part 2 (May)	2	15	4	68
Summer Camp (Sept.)	2	4	5	30
Mining Engineering Part 1 (Dec.)	4	23	7	189
1981				
Mining Engineering Part 2 (April)	2	16	7	126
Mining Geology Part 2 (May)	2	12	4	56
Summer Camp (July)	3	9	14	168
Mining Engineering Part 1 (Dec.)	4	21	7	175
GRAND TOTAL	–	–		1710

Limited time was available for the rehabilitation activities and student groups were generally inexperienced. These factors made it necessary to organise operations in great detail for safe and satisfactory progress to be achieved. The organisation of the first Summer Camp from 23 July to 4 August 1978 involved a daily work chart that directed each of the four small groups to different parts of Long Adit; the chart listed the operations, work listing and scheduling. A similar programme was followed for Mitchell Adit, and this pattern provided the model for subsequent Summer Camps in Phase One rehabilitation.

Activities in the short vacation field course programmes were divided into, (a) the practical work involved in the rehabilitation of an old abandoned mine and (b) developing an understanding of the geology of the gold lodes and how they had been mined in Roman and modern times. Understandably, the main emphasis in the early years was placed upon the safe re-opening of the mine and that period of the rehabilitation was generally entered into with enthusiasm by all the students involved.

The short vacation field courses formed part of first and second year student teaching programmes. However, the progress made in the early years allowed final year and postgraduate students to pursue project study with exercises in geological and geotechnical mapping, geochemical and geophysical exploration, ore sampling and assaying, and mine surveying, ventilation, and development planning.

The main achievements of Phase One operations are shown in the following illustrations, these being a small selection from the many photographs that recorded the progress made in the different activities.

1. Mine re-entry operations
2. Posting warning notices
3. Mine drainage/Water control
4. Adit gates construction
5. Railtrack installation

6. Waste bin construction
7. Provision of services
8. Mine Office construction
9. Geological exploration
10. Workers and Visitors

1. RE-ENTRY OPERATIONS AT LONG ADIT

Clearing away vegetation and fallen debris from the entrance to Long Adit (*c.*1978).

Removal of collapsed rock, resetting of roof support and drainage of the flooded section of Long Adit (1978).

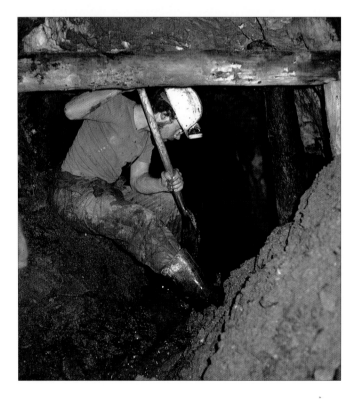

2. POSTING WARNING NOTICES

Bilingual warning notices erected by Professor Brian Smart (on left) and colleague at entrance to Long Adit (1978).

3. (a) MINE DRAINAGE ARRANGEMENTS

Clearing and levelling the entry to Long Adit with drainage channel on left (1978).

Pump installation in Long Adit (1978).

3. (b) MINEWATER CONTROL

Mine drainage sump construction with Professor Keith Williams on right. This was the main sump collecting minewater via Long Adit (*c.*1979).

Completed sump showing water entry via pipe column from Long Adit and V-notch at exit for measurement of flow into the outgoing pipe column (*c.*1979).

4. ADIT GATES CONSTRUCTION

To satisfy the requirements of mining legislation, gates were erected to prevent unauthorised entry to the mine. The first completed lockable gate was placed at the entry to Long Adit.

Completed gate installation at Long Adit (*c.*1979).

Gate construction at Mill Adit with Professor Keith Williams leading its construction (*c.*1980).

Gate construction at the top of the mine workings (*c.*1980).

5. INSTALLATION OF RAILTRACK FOR REMOVAL OF DEBRIS

Commencement of railtrack installation with graded aggregate being used to give stability (*c.*1980). Long Adit was part of the route for clearing waste rock and old materials from all parts of the mine.

Railtrack installation and levelling for ensuring stability of mine vehicle movement (*c.*1980).

Completed installation of ballasted railtrack at exit from Long Adit leading to waste bin transfer point (*c.*1981).

Completed installation of railtrack in Long Adit with drainage channel on right (*c.*1981).

6. CONSTRUCTION OF WASTE ROCK BIN / TRANSFER POINT

Excavation of an embankment.

Commencement of concrete emplacement of base.

Breeze block walls and concrete floor (*c.1980*).

7. SERVICES PROVISION – Electricity, Water and Compressed Air

Mechanical trench digging for installation of electricity and water supplies to the mine (*c*.1980).

Manual trench digging to complete the job. The air compressor in the background is supplying air to drilling equipment in Long Adit (*c*.1980).

8. CONSTRUCTION OF MINE OFFICE

Laying the footings for the first half of the Mine Office with Dr Alwyn Annels leading its design and construction (*c.*1979).

First half of mine office erected and operational as the meetings and communication base, and first aid station (*c.*1980).

Mine office in summer time, the surrounding area being laid with new aggregate (c.1980).

The symbolic drillstone erected in the Open Pit providing a link with the 1930s period of mining. The drillstone was originally used for testing the sharpness of drillbits (c.1980).

9. GEOLOGICAL EXPLORATION

The development of an operational base at the gold mine also allowed other closely related activities to proceed at Dolaucothi. These included geochemical and geological exploration over the whole of the Cothi valley and adjacent hills. This led to a diamond drilling programme which commenced in 1979 and was funded by the Anglo-Canadian Exploration Company Ltd. (ACE).

(i) Locating the drill rig at the drilling site.

(ii) Raising the drill rig mast.

Diamond drilling activities on the hillsides around the Dolaucothi Gold Mine as part of a comprehensive geological exploration programme under the direction and supervision of Dr Alwyn Annels (*c.*1979).

(iii) Drilling in progress.

(iv) Drill core recovery.

10. WORKERS AND VISITORS

A group of academic staff, postgraduate and undergraduate students at commencement of rehabilitation during the first Summer Camp (July 1978).

Part One Mining Engineering undergraduate student leaders celebrating completion of task by their groups (December 1978).

Dr Alwyn Annels with notice board information for public visitors, and a 'donations box' for student benefit (*c.*1978).

Vice-Chancellor and staff on a visit to Dolaucothi Gold Mine (*c.*1979). *Left to right:* Prof. Brian Smart, Prof. Lyn Evans, Dr C. W. L. Bevan (Vice-Chancellor), University Chauffeur, Dr Alwyn Annels and Dr Alun Isaac.

Professor Brian Smart with Mr Peter
Mitchell, Land Agent for the
National Trust, discussing progress
being made in the mine
rehabilitation (*c.*1979).

Professor Albert Davies, Principal
District Inspector of Mines and
Quarries, Wales, with Professor
Kenneth Brown, Head of
Department of Mineral
Exploitation, Cardiff University
(*c.*1980).

The support of the project by VIPs
was a strong encouragement to all
involved in the rehabilitation.

VI

PHASE TWO:
EDUCATION AND MINE DEVELOPMENT
1984–1988

SHORT VACATION FIELD COURSES

The practical engineering emphasis of early rehabilitation activity enabled longer term objectives to be pursued in Phases Two and Three, as shown in the accompanying photographs. Summarising, these objectives were:

University teaching and research: to provide facilities for teaching and research into the scientific and practical aspects of mining geology, mining engineering and minerals engineering;

Conservation: to conserve a unique mining location and broaden its technical and general appeal;

Public relations: to make information generally available of the nature of past and future mining and mineral science activities as an aid to public visitor interest.

The short vacation field course of December 1986 realised the first stages of field course training for students of Part One Mining Engineering and Part Two Mining Geology (see Appendix A4.1). The schedule of activities involved three academic staff, four postgraduate students and thirty undergraduate students in a programme of experimental work; much of this is shown in the illustrations that follow. Appendix A4.2 illustrates the organisation of the same course for the following year of students with its development incorporating additional equipment and new ideas.

1. SURFACE EXPLORATION

Geophysics earth resistivity survey on hillside above the gold mine with Senior Technician, Peter Fisher supervising 2nd year Earth Science students. Note the village of Pumsaint in centre ground to the north (1986).

Determination of geological anomalies using geophysical techniques (1986).

2. MINE SURVEYING

Mine surveying in the Roman adits (1986).

3. GEOTECHNICAL ENGINEERING

Geotechnical exercises at Middle Adit (1986).

(i) Rock strength testing using a Schmidt Hammer.

(ii) Measuring the orientation of rock bedding planes using a Clar compass.

4. UNDERGROUND EXPLORATION

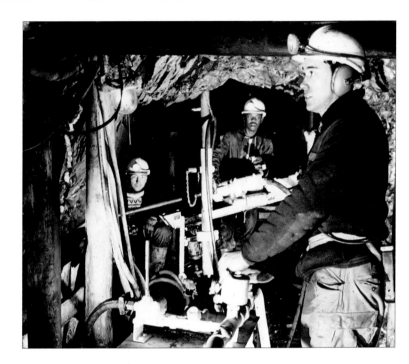

Geological exploration activity in Long Adit (1986).

(i) Core drilling in Long Adit.

(ii) Core recovery, examination and storage.

5. MINERALS ENGINEERING

(i) Manual crushing of ore samples.

(ii) Shaking table separation of gold particles from crushed ore.

(iii) Use of a froth flotation cell to produce a concentrate (*c.1986*).

6. (a) MINING ENGINEERING PRACTICE

(i) Rock drilling.

(ii) Support setting in an orebody zone (*c.*1986).

6. (b) MINING ENGINEERING PRACTICE

(iii) *Left:* Support setting in weak roof zone (*c.1986*).

Right: Ladder access to working platform in orebody.

(iv) Wooden shaft ladder and platform installation.

7. MINEWATER CONTROL

(i) Construction of water storage facility for rock drilling and fire fighting (*c.1986*).

(ii) Measurement of mine water flow using a V notch.

8. SITE ACCESS ACTIVITIES

(i) Surface pathway construction from Open Pit to Mitchell Adit (*c.*1986).

(ii) Erecting safety fencing along surface pathway (*c.*1986).

The activities illustrated on the previous pages brought together first year mining engineering and second year mining geology students who were then integrated within six groups. Each group followed a broadly similar programme of lectures and practical activities on different days of the seven-day course. In this course and those that followed, broader-based engineering visits were organised to nearby sites of engineering interest such as the large Llyn Brianne reservoir and the old lead/zinc mine workings at Rhandirmwyn. These visits were designed to provide interest and light relief as did the festivities that usually accompanied end-of-term Christmas and Easter celebrations at the Dolaucothi Farm Barn and nearby hostelries.

Undergraduate group viewing the slipway at the Llyn Brianne Reservoir that controls the flow of the River Tywi near Rhandirmwyn, Carmarthenshire (c.1986).

Surface building foundations and spoil heaps at the 19th century lead/zinc mine workings, Rhandirmwyn (c.1986).

Surface building foundations and spoil heaps at the 19th century lead/zinc mine workings, Rhandirmwyn (*c.*1986).

Accommodation for staff and students was organised in the same way as in earlier years with a variety of places provided by the National Trust and the community of Pumsaint and District. The welcome from the people of the area was always warm and encouraging, and with much interest shown in the gold-mine project. However, showering facilities were variable with the solitary mine office shower voted the worst, those in the National Trust Barn a little better, and Llandovery College showers, the best.

Dolaucothi Lodge, home of Tom and Morfydd Cleminson, who provided wonderful meals for staff and postgraduate students in the early days of rehabilitation (*c.*1978).

Catering was a mix of 'bed and breakfast' at houses in the locality with self-catering the feature of the evening meal in the National Trust barn accommodation at Dolaucothi Farm. The fare produced for the whole group by students organised on a strict rota basis, was always interesting and often experimental, both in content and preparation! However, after a day's hard work, most food disappeared quickly and the plates usually required little washing up after the meal!

Dolaucothi Farm barn, also in the early days, where cattle were housed on the ground floor . . . and undergraduate students on the first floor (1978).

The Farm barn after renovation, with the cattle now housed elsewhere and the students provided with much improved facilities (c.1982).

Self-catering by student groups on a military style rota basis (*c.*1985).

Calculations in the Barn following the day's work, prior to some liquid refreshment in one of the many local hostelries (*c.*1985). Note the decorated Christmas tree in the background!

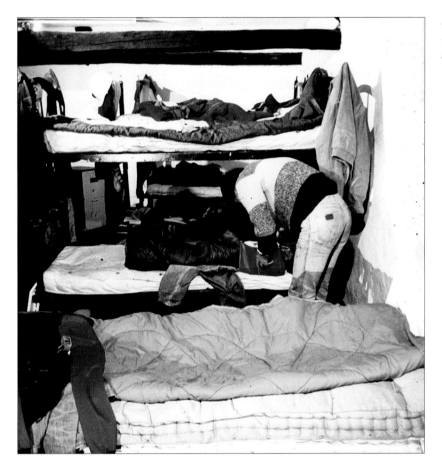

Quality bunk beds in the dormitory, the area also being maintained on a daily rota basis (*c.*1985).

LONG VACATION SUMMER CAMPS

Similar field course activities that took place throughout the four-year second phase of Field Centre development were enhanced during this time by work in the two to three weeks-long Summer Camps. In addition, the enthusiasm of the student body encouraged several weekend visits to supplement the general progress of development.

Usually, summer work was undertaken by the more experienced undergraduate students, under the supervision of academic and technical staff and with the assistance of postgraduate students. Underground operations required to be properly directed and monitored in line with appropriate mining legislation. The Department's technical staff usually performed surface and underground operations that required mechanical and electrical engineering knowledge.

Project work included the enlargement of the Mine Office, the building of the Workshop Laboratory, the laying of rail track and the installation of mine lighting.

Dr Annels, Dr Gordon Kingston and colleagues (not in picture) laying the foundation and concrete floor for the enlargement of the mine office to incorporate a teaching facility (*c.*1983).

(i) Commencement of the construction of a workshop/ laboratory led by Dr Annels with undergraduate students laying the footings for the building (*c.*1983).

The various operations undertaken in the construction of the workshop/laboratory that was originally the garage of a local resident and dismantled by staff and students (*c*.1983).

(ii) Workshop/laboratory skeleton framework under construction. Much of the framework was constructed in Cardiff by Dr Annels and subsequently transported to Dolaucothi.

(iii) Felt and corrugated sheet cladding of the exterior roof and walls of the workshop/laboratory.

(iv) Workshop/laboratory construction completed and painted.

Clearing waste rock from the upper levels of the mine workings for removal via the internal shaft (*c.*1980).

Loading of waste rock into a mine car at the bottom of the internal shaft (*c.*1980).

Enjoyment of task completion by postgraduate students (*c.*1980).

Mine lighting system installed in Long Adit (*c.*1980).

Professor Brian Smart (on left), Dr
Alun Isaac (centre) and Dr Alwyn
Annels (background), relaxing and
discussing ways of enhancing
student enjoyment of further tasks
(*c*.1981).

Professor Smart making the first
inspection of the internal shaft
linking Long Adit with Mitchell
Adit some 30m above.

At bottom of shaft.　　　　　　Near the top (with white knuckles).

Regrading the entry to Mitchell Adit with the assistance and under the supervision of Tom Cleminson of Ogofau Lodge (*c.*1981).

Installing a drainage column at the adit portal (*c.*1981).

HM Mines Inspector with mine official at Mitchell Adit portal on a general inspection of the mine following completion of improved access operations (c.1981).

THE PROPOSED LINK TUNNEL

One of the major projects commenced during a mining engineering vacation field course in early 1987 (see Appendix A4.3) and continued during that summer was the proposed linkage of the Long and Middle Adits by an 80 metre long tunnel. This work required surface and underground surveys for tunnel direction and gradient, and for its depth below surface to be established. Various planning permissions were required for this work from the local authorities and the Police. I.C.I.'s Nobel's Explosive Company also provided advice and donated equipment and explosives materials.

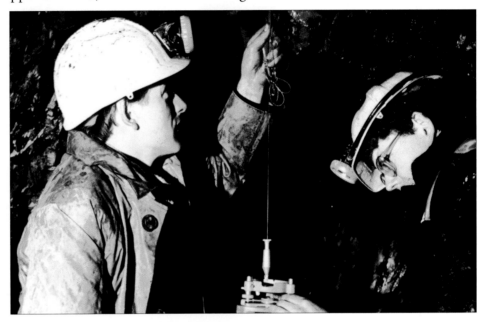

(i) Survey work at the junction of the proposed tunnel in Long Adit.

(ii) Drilling of holes for insertion of explosives as part of the first blast at the entry point to the linking tunnel.

(iii) Measurement of airflow quantity by anemometer. Note the roof supports erected at the junction of the new tunnel drivage, and the drillholes that were prepared for the first round of explosives blasting (1987).

(iv) Measurement of humidity in the mine air using a Storrow's whirling hygrometer (1987).

(v) Clearing broken rock after the first round of blasting. Note the prominent quartz veins exposed after the blast (1987).

(vi) Removal of broken rock to the waste bin prior to installation of mechanical haulage facilities (1987).

(vii) Removal of rock from waste bin to an on site spoil heap (1987).

Dr Edward Hellewell (front centre) with postgraduate student leaders and Mining Engineering undergraduate student group when the link tunnel project commenced (1987).

Throughout the time that the staff and students worked at the goldmine, the tenants of Dolaucothi Farm, Tegwyn and Iris Williams, usually provided and organised accommodation and catering arrangements that satisfied everyone. The heavy nature of the work at the Field Centre required appropriate support and the University appreciated the care and attention given to its staff and students by the people of Pumsaint and District.

THE EQUIPPING PERIOD

With contraction of the coal industry in Wales, opportunities arose for the acquisition of old mining equipment and in this respect, the advice and support of British Coal, South Wales, was significant in continuing the momentum of the project. Other links with the wider mining industry resulted in the donation of a surface drill rig and diamond drilling equipment for geological exploration from the Anglo Canadian Exploration Company (ACE). Mining manufacturer, Atlas Copco GB Ltd., also donated rock drilling equipment for tunnel drivage operations.

Delivery of equipment from closed coalmines in south Wales (*c.*1980–*c.*1988).

Unloading an approved magazine for storage of explosives and detonators. Only limited amounts of both were permitted.

Air compressor and air line donated by Atlas Copco (GB) Ltd. together with rock drilling machines and associated equipment (*c.*1980–*c.*1983).

Undoubtedly the greatest dramatic impact in terms of equipment donation resulted from a meeting between University staff and a senior member of the Rio Tinto Zinc (RTZ) Mining Company. The RTZ member indicated that the possibility existed for the acquisition of a complete 1930s vintage mine surface arrangement that included buildings, shaft winding gear and compressors from a mine in North Wales. The discussions that followed this meeting resulted in a joint University/National Trust visit to the closed Olwyn Goch lead/zinc mine in the Halkyn area near Holywell in North Wales. Subsequently, Courtaulds, the Mine owners generously donated to the National Trust an assemblage of surface and underground equipment for installation at Dolaucothi.

The National Trust decided to progress the transfer and erection of the Olwyn Goch Mine machinery and equipment and sought the advice of consultancy services. The John Brown Tourism Services report, the Michael Quinion Interpretive Appendix to the Brown report and the later A. T. Herbert report, 1986, all concluded that the Dolaucothi Gold Mine site would be much more attractive to its members and the general public as a result of this development. The University wholeheartedly supported the decision.

The Herbert report provided an inventory with photographs of the equipment at the Olwyn Goch mine. An extract of this report (see Appendix A5) shows the care taken in the work with details recorded not only of a twin drum shaft winder hoist but also fire buckets, a set of spanners and a three-legged stool. The total collection of 1930s vintage mining equipment included the shaft headgear with cages and winding ropes, a winding engine, three large capacity air compressors, workshop equipment, mine cars, locomotives, tunnelling equipment and a host of related equipment.

The considerable administrative and financial aspects of the transfer of this equipment were undertaken by the National Trust who organised the necessary funding with substantial grant-aid from the Welsh Development Agency, the Wales Tourist Board, the Science Museum, London, the Manpower Services Commission, various private sponsors and from its own resources.

Olwyn Goch Mine Shaft winding head frame before its removal from Rhydymwyn, Clwyd, in North Wales (1986).

Winding Engine house at Olwyn Goch Mine before removal to Dolaucothi (1986).

Compressed air receivers and related pipework at Olwyn Goch Mine (1986).

Erection of Olwyn Goch Mine shaft headframe at Dolaucothi. The lamproom, mechanical engineering shop and compressor house are shown as erected prior to that of the shaft equipment (1987).

Installation of the shaft headframe wheels and cage winding ropes (1987).

Shaft headframe, winding engine house and workshops in position (1987).

Installation of this equipment commenced in July 1987 and within three months, the site had taken on a totally changed appearance. The six buildings at the site in September 1987, shown overleaf, were designated as:

Mine Office: extended by University staff in 1986 for operational control of surface and underground activities;

Mine Workshop/Laboratory: erected by University staff in 1986 for use as an equipment maintenance centre, and as a laboratory for drill core analysis and structural interpretation of the geology;

Visitor Reception Centre: erected by contractors for the National Trust in 1986 for public visitor reception in the summer months, with approximately 25,000 visitors passing through the mine in 1987;

Compressor House: erected by contractors for the National Trust in 1987 for display purposes;

Workshops and storage buildings: erected by contractors for the National Trust in 1987 for display purposes;

Winding Engine House and Headframe: erected by contractors for the National Trust in 1987 for the subsequent installation of a fully operational double-drum winding engine, also for display purposes.

Mine Office/Lecture Room (1986). (Covered perspex mine model in front of office).

Mine Workshop/Laboratory (1986).

National Trust Visitor Centre (1986).

General view of the mine surface, now established to resemble a 1930s mine site in traditional red lead colour of the period (December 1988).

Assortment of miscellaneous mining equipment from Olwyn Goch Mine. Note the power loading shovel (centre right) that was later transferred to the University for repair and renewal (1987).

Other activities in Phase Two included the installation of an electricity generating facility, general maintenance work, further opening up of ore zones requiring roof stabilization measures, rail system development and the addition of improved facilities.

Construction by Dr Keith Williams with postgraduate students of an electricity generator house to provide a three phase supply to the mine (c.1984).

Undergraduate students carrying out maintenance activity on the shaft winding engine (*c.*1990).

Specialist engineers at the air compressor house with Brian Parry of the National Trust (centre), who was responsible for general site and equipment maintenance (*c.*1990).

Maintenance work at the mine drainage sump outside Long Adit (*c.*1990).

Dr Peter Brabham clearing vegetation at the entrance to Mill Adit during the annual site maintenance programme (*c.*1990).

Development of the Long Adit rail track to connect with the waste rock bin, the workshop/laboratory and the mine surface (*c.*1990).

New lamp room built on to the rear of the workshop/laboratory with Dr Annels shown erecting the internal cladding of the latter (*c.*1990).

The construction of a gift
shop/tearoom and National Trust
office on the upper floor completed
the site buildings, shown prior to
being painted in site colour (*c.*1990).

Although Phase Two activity was completed substantially by 1988, similar work continued in the third phase of Field Centre development. The list below provides a record of the various periods when the Department was present at the site.

PHASE TWO/THREE DEVELOPMENT ACTIVITY, 1984/1990

December	1985	Part 1 Mining Engineering Field Course
March	1986	Part 2 Mining Engineering Field Course
December	1986	Part 1 Mining Engineering/ Part 2 Mining Geology Field Course
March	1987	Part 2 Mining Engineering Field Course
December	1987	Part 1 Mining & Minerals Engineering/ Part 2 Mining Geology Field Course
September	1988	Part 2 Mining Engineering Field Course
April	1989	Part 2 Mining Engineering Field Course
April	1990	Part 2 Mining Engineering field Course
June	1990	Summer Camp 1990

Throughout the course of both phases of activity described above, the team approach of academic and technical staff with postgraduate and undergraduate students was a major element in the successful rehabilitation and development operations.

VII

PHASE THREE: NEW DEVELOPMENTS
1988–1999

CARDIFF SCHOOL OF ENGINEERING

The 1980s saw major changes at British Universities with Government emphasis placed on rationalisation of resources, teaching quality and research output. Long-established universities were required to concentrate their teaching and research activities in the most cost-effective manner with mergers of departments into larger units. Similarly, new universities resulted from the combination of smaller colleges into enlarged structures.

National surveys of subject teaching provision in, for example, Departments of Geology, Metallurgy and Mining and Minerals Engineering were conducted by Government-appointed teams of external specialists, which resulted in closure of departments and consolidation of teaching at prescribed locations. Universities were also designated as either teaching centres with some research activity, or as research centres of excellence based on the assessment of teaching quality, research activity, and effectiveness of funding.

Within this new framework, the long-established University College Cardiff (UCC) and the younger University of Wales Institute of Science and Technology (UWIST) merged in 1988 to become the University of Wales College of Cardiff. One of the schools to be formed in the new College was the Cardiff School of Engineering which brought together the different engineering disciplines of the former colleges.

The new School was divided into five Divisions, namely Civil Engineering, Mechanical Engineering, Electrical & Electronic Engineering, Structural & Architectural Engineering, and Materials & Minerals Engineering. This arrangement enabled all first year students to study together a number of subjects in their Foundation Year, followed by two-year specialist programmes to Degree level. This concentration of large first year groups led to the further development of teaching at the Mining field Centre that was then renamed the Dolaucothi Field Centre.

During the period of rationalisation and merger, a small core of Mining Engineering and Minerals Engineering staff remained within the new School. However, the decision was taken by the Mining Geology staff to transfer to the Department of Geology. Colleagues in both Schools who had actively pursued the development of the Field Centre at Dolaucothi, decided to continue their work there, resulting in further involvement of Engineering and Geology students.

SCHOOL OF EARTH, OCEAN AND PLANETARY SCIENCES

Those staff who were principally involved with the teaching of the Exploration and Mining geology degree scheme and associated postgraduate research, transferred in 1989 to the Department of Geology, later renamed in 1991, the School of Earth Sciences and subsequently to its present name, the School of Earth, Ocean and Planetary Sciences. This allowed for the teaching of aspects of Mining Engineering to students of mining geology.

From this new base, the teaching of mining-related sciences continued, initially at undergraduate level and then, in 1994, at postgraduate level, with the introduction of a new M.Sc. in Mineral Resources. This degree brought together all the disciplines needed for mine feasibility studies including mining, geo-technical, hydrogeological, environmental and minerals engineering. Heavy emphasis was also placed on mineral resource evaluation and financial modelling for mining operations. This degree scheme was taught by ex-members of the former Mineral Exploitation Department, by mining consultants (especially from SRK Consulting (UK) Ltd) and by Earth Sciences staff.

This new development resulted in the increased use of the Dolaucothi Gold Mine for practical training, either on week-long formal courses or shorter field visits. Funding received from both the University and from Anglesey Mining Plc, enabled diamond drilling to continue on site within the open pit area and also below the two Roman Adits to the southwest. Students and technical staff gained invaluable experience in the planning and control of drilling operations including the operation of the rig itself under the supervision of an experienced diamond driller. Holes were internally surveyed and core from them logged in the mine's workshop/laboratory. Between 1985 and 2000, fourteen holes were completed at depths of up to 140m below surface providing much new infor-mation on the geological controls of gold mineralization and the nature of the gold lodes. The existing adits provided students with experience in underground surveying and geological mapping.

GEOLOGICAL RESEARCH ACTIVITY, 1970–1991

Prior to and throughout the time as University leaseholder at Dolaucothi, a consistent and productive effort was made to determine the nature of gold deposition and geological structure. The results of a continuous programme of geochemical exploration and diamond drilling under the direction of Mining Geology staff are summarised in Section 3 of the 3rd edition of the publication, *Dolaucothi Gold Mines – Geology and Mining History*. A more detailed account has been published that explains the geology and genesis of the gold ores in the Dolaucothi region (Annels and Roberts, 1989).

This research has revealed that the mineralized zone lies within a 100m wide, northeasterly trending belt in which the black shales and siltstones have been intensely folded and thrusted into a series of up to five stacked anticlinal folds. The shales were originally deposited some 438 million years ago. Within this zone there are several highly pyritized horizons, the main one (the Pyrite Lode) is up to l.5m thick. These horizons have been locally enriched in gold and arsenopyrite deposited from hot iron, sulphur and arsenic bearing solutions. A massive coarse-grained body of quartz or saddle reef has invaded one of these fold structures and is referred to as the Roman Lode. Closely associated with this reef and usually in its footwall, is a broader mineralized zone in which the host rocks are invaded by a stockwork of thin quartz-carbonate vein or 'stringers' and sub-parallel 'Quartz leaders', most of which also carry gold. The main reef extends tor some 250m along strike, reaching up to six metres thick in places and dips at approximately 28° beneath the Cothi Valley to a depth of at least 150m.

FURTHER EXPLORATION ACTIVITY, 1995–2000

During the period 1995 to 2000, a number of advanced exploration techniques described below, were employed around the mine under the supervision of Earth Sciences staff.

- Compilation of all known soil geochemical data into a Geographical Information database. Computer-based maps were produced of the data and the levels of Arsenic in the soil were used as an indicator of the presence of Arsenopyrite anomalies in the bedrock.
- During the mid-1990s, the mine was used as a test site for various geophysical methods of investigation including Radar and Electromagnetics.

- The consulting company, SRK (UK) Ltd., supported a full environmental and physical mapping programme of the 1930s waste tailings dams. The dams were surveyed and drilled to their base together with geophysical resistivity and radar surveys. Water samples were analysed to assess the arsenic content and samples of sandy tailings were assayed to determine the potential residual gold content.
- Electrical resistivity imaging was carried out in the Open Pit area to assess the thickness of post-Roman backfill.
- Using Ordnance Survey digital terrain models and Getmapping digital Air Imagery, virtual three-dimensional landscape models were constructed of the Cothi valley.

TECHNICAL STAFF ACTIVITIES

Throughout the redevelopment of Dolaucothi Gold Mine into an educational field centre, the Department's technical staff played a major role. Their knowledge, skills and enthusiasm were invaluable in the development of teaching programmes, machinery procurement, installation and maintenance, and general transportation duties. It is a tribute to their flexibility and willingness that they were prepared to involve themselves in a new and exciting activity, particularly when their personal training and previous work experience did not take place in a mining environment.

Much of the equipment recovered from old mines needed repair prior to its use by staff and students. In particular, some of the Olwyn Goch Mine equipment from North Wales was relatively old and had lain rusting for some time before its move to Dolaucothi. A number of items were transferred from the gold mine to the Departmental workshops where they were dismantled and replacement parts fitted. They were then painted, tested, and returned to the Field Centre for use in the mine. Some of these items of renewed equipment, such as the compressed air power loader and the electric battery locomotive were sited on the mine surface as an attractive display feature for visitors. The repair and installation of lighting, signalling and communication systems also formed part of a programme of good health and safety standards for all persons entering the underground workings.

Eimco power loading shovel at the Department of Mineral Exploitation workshops at Cardiff University (*c.*1988).

Overhaul of the Eimco power loader by Departmental technicians, Jeffrey Rowlands and Alan Davies, at the University workshop (*c.*1988).

Various items of mechanical equipment following overhaul and testing at the University workshop in readiness for transfer back to Dolaucothi Gold Mine in 1989.

Eimco compressed air power loader for tunnelling operations, overhauled, tested and painted.

Single stage centrifugal pump for mine drainage.

Double and single drum haulage winches for transporting materials within mine and loaded mine cars out. David Glinn, School technician, shown testing equipment in readiness for return to Dolaucothi.

Electric battery locomotive overhauled at the University (David Glinn, technician, c.1988).

Battery locomotive in use at Dolaucothi mine surface (Alan Davies, technician, c.1989).

As in the University laboratories, the technicians at Dolaucothi were an important element of student learning activity. They directed and supervised student group activities such as surveying, core drilling and geotechnical surveys, provided instruction in the use of instrumentation and equipment, and transported groups and equipment between different study locations. They also provided an information and communication link between equipment manufacturers and staff, and also a social link between staff and students. The contribution of technical staff was invaluable and much appreciated by academic staff and students.

DEVELOPMENT OF TEACHING PROGRAMMES

The three phases of rehabilitation and development activity at Dolaucothi are clearly identifiable, namely, Phase One 1978–1984, Phase Two 1984–1988 and Phase Three 1988–1999. However, there was much overlap between these phases in the development of educational programmes. While Phase One was essentially that of mine rehabilitation, it included elements of academic work for Mining Geology, Mining Engineering and Minerals Engineering students.

While Phase Two completed the rehabilitation of the mine, it also continued the mine development programme. An important feature also during the short vacation field courses, was the upgrading of the undergraduate teaching programmes with increased academic content. While first and second year students of all the Mineral Exploitation Department's sections followed activities similar to those in Phase One, third year students were directed to project work and postgraduate students to research studies. Sponsorship support for geological exploration was particularly helpful for the Mining Geology undergraduates and postgraduates.

The teaching and learning experience built up during the first ten years together with the addition of mining machinery and equipment enabled further academic development to take place in Phase Three. With the formation of the School of Engineering, in 1988, field courses were organised for the first year students of the new Divisions of Civil and Structural Engineering, Architectural Engineering and Environmental Engineering. This involved larger numbers of staff and students than previously on mainly surface surveying tasks.

School of Engineering Staff and
First Year students (1989).
(Photograph taken from the top of
the shaft headframe).

Staff and students in Mitchell Adit
with Dr Adnan Sabir and Dr Terry
Roberts of Civil and Structural
Engineering Division and Dr Alun
Isaac, Materials and Minerals
Division (1989).

School of Engineering academic and technical staff, postgraduate and first year undergraduate students (1990).

Dr Stephen Bentley and first year student setting up survey equipment (1990).

First Year Engineering students on field survey operations using a variety of survey equipment (1990).

One of the challenges of this development was that of accommodation and catering on and off-site. Numbers of up to 100 students were eventually housed and catered for at the University College, Lampeter. In addition, the National Trust tea-room facilities were a welcome part of any day's activities for all involved, with the franchise catering arrangement led by Mrs Iris Williams, the Manager, and her neighbours from the community of Pumsaint and District.

Mrs Iris Williams, Franchise holder and Catering Manager of the National Trust Tearoom, the National Trust Visitor Centre, being shown in the background (*c.*1990).

Mrs Williams and one of her staff (granddaughter) at work in the tearoom (*c.*1990).

Second and third year students of Mining Engineering and Mining Geology (now part of the new Earth Sciences Department at Cardiff) continued to follow the well-established patterns of earlier field courses. Third year students were required to submit a Special Project report as part of their degree assessment and this resulted in high quality research leading to many excellent proposals for further studies and even mine development.

The title of one such Special Project, *The Equipping Phase at the Mining Field Centre, Ogofau Gold Mine* (Crossley, 1988*)*, was a good example of how students were linking the academic and practical aspects of their higher education. There were many similar examples from the different subject areas in final year studies. This practice followed that introduced in the early years of Departmental interest at Dolaucothi, one of the first such Honours Degree projects being entitled, *Ogofau Gold Mine* (Williams, 1970).

The eventual demise in the teaching of the Mining Engineering degree course at Cardiff came with the reorganisation of the two University of Wales Colleges in Cardiff and the subsequent birth of the School of Engineering in 1988.

END OF AN ERA, 1891–1991: Cover of the Programme of the Final Dinner of alumni and students of Mining Engineering, Minerals Engineering and Mining Geology at the traditional venue, the Park Hotel, Cardiff (1992).

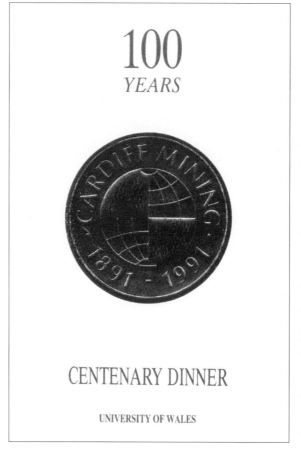

The contribution of Cardiff students from 1891 to 1991 to the national and international mining industries was celebrated by alumni of the old *Jones's Heading* (a Society named after the much-loved Professor T. David Jones, Head of Department from 1936 to 1947) together with their successors in the *Mining Society* (1948–1968) and the *Minex Society* (1969–1991). A Final Annual Dinner was held in the traditional venue, the Park Hotel, Cardiff, that provided a fitting end to a century of progress in mining education and in the world mining industries.

However, while seeing the end of mining education,

the new Cardiff School of Engineering provided the opportunity for innovation in teaching and the integration of staff and students from different engineering and other disciplines. One such innovation in 1991 was the introduction for undergraduates of four-year Masters Degree (M.Eng.) courses; this was in addition to the traditional three-year undergraduate degree courses (B.Eng.).

One subject area of the M.Eng. course in Civil Engineering brought together elements of geology and engineering into the subject of geotechnical engineering. The Field Centre provided the facility for studying this subject in a realistic geotechnical environment. From 1992–1999, student numbers in the new M.Eng. course were restricted, to ensure careful development of the programme before leading to its more general availability.

During this formative period, the fourth year of M.Eng. studies included a five-day period of field study at Dolaucothi Gold Mine. Reports were required from each of several groups, each group comprising four or five students, on pre-feasibility studies for the further development of the Gold Mine. The studies included projects such as the design of a surface transportation scheme, the linking of two or more mine tunnels, or the introduction of underground self-guiding routes for visitors. The report from one group, entitled, *Geotechnical Design: Link Drivage Study* (Benson, 1999) was an example of student group activity in a field setting.

Civil Engineering (M.Eng.) students setting up survey instrumentation (*c.*1996).

Civil Engineering (M.Eng.) students recording the results of survey work (*c.*1996).

Civil Engineering (M.Eng.) students finalising computation of survey results in the mine office (*c.*1994).

Civil Engineering (M.Eng.) students at the final evening's barbecue (c.1996).

Civil Engineering (M.Eng.) student campfire and barbecue celebrations (c.1996).

In contrast to their field centre activities, the Civil Engineering students (M.Eng., 1996–1998) at the Annual Dinner of the South Wales Institute of Engineers, Park Hotel, Cardiff (1998).

Sainsbury Trust Summer School students standing in the portal of Middle Adit on a visit to Dolaucothi as part of publicity and student recruitment activity (c.1990s).

During Phase Three, the Field Centre also provided new and significant benefits for the University at Cardiff as an interesting venue for prospective students from schools under the Mineral Industries Manpower and Careers Unit scheme. These students were invited to the Field Centre as part of their exposure to careers opportunities. Students from other Universities, viz., Nottingham, Glamorgan and Leicester, were also involved in field courses at Dolaucothi (see list below). The educational and public relations aspects of these links were particularly helpful for student recruitment and also generated additional finance from the hire of the Centre. This was also supported by the sale of the University staff publication, *The Dolaucothi Gold Mines: Geology and Mining History* (Annels & Burnham, 1st Ed. 1983; 2nd Ed. 1986; 3rd Ed. 1995).

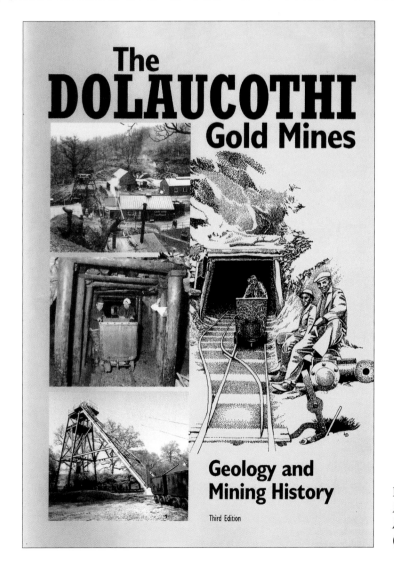

Front cover of the booklet, *The Dolaucothi Gold Mines: Geology & Mining History, 3rd Edition, 1995* (first published 1983).

ANNUAL USE OF THE DOLAUCOTHI FIELD CENTRE,
1992–1999

September   Geological Field Visit.
M.Sc. Mineral Resources, Cardiff.

September   2nd Year Applied Science Field Course,
Leicester University.

September   M.Sc. Exploration and Mining Geology Field Course,
Leicester University.

December   M.Sc. Mineral Resources Field Course; Drilling,
core logging, underground mapping,
Cardiff University.

March   Part 3 B.Sc.Exploration Geology Exploration
Design Project, Cardiff.

March   Part 4 M.Eng Civil Engineering Field Course
Geotechnical Design Project, Cardiff.

March   Part 2 B.Sc. Exploration Geology, Field Course,
Cardiff University.

March   Part 1 B.Eng. Architectural and Environmental
Engineering Field Course, surface survey work,
Cardiff University.

April   Part 2 B.Sc.Surveying for Resource Development
Field Course Mine surveying exercises,
University of Glamorgan.

July   Summer Camp, maintenance and development
activities, Cardiff University.

July/August   Part 2 B.Sc. Exploration Geology, Project work,
Cardiff University

An interesting extension of educational activity at the Field Centre occurred in 1988, linking Phases Two and Three, which introduced the area of Primary education. Academic staff of the School made proposals for a tripartite research study between the National Trust, the Gwent College of Higher Education (now the University of Wales College, Newport) and the Cardiff School of Engineering. The study aimed to produce education resources for teachers at Primary schools in Wales, this being described fully in the next chapter entitled, *The Dolaucothi Education Project.*

THE PROPOSED MINERALS PROCESSING PILOT PLANT

Also in 1988, a further development of gold mine activity was considered that related to the proposed tunnel drivage linking Long and Mill Adits. At that time, interest by mining entrepreneurs in reopening the old Gwynfynydd Gold Mine near Dolgellau failed to materialise for a number of reasons including lack of finance. As at the Olwyn Goch mine near Halkyn in North Wales, there was a range of mining equipment awaiting disposal. A decision was made by the staff of the School of Earth, Ocean and Planetary Sciences and the School of Engineering to obtain the minerals processing equipment so that any gold ore extracted from the proposed link drivage could be processed.

Academic and technical staff and postgraduate students were responsible for loading the equipment from the Gwynfynydd Mine and then transporting and receiving the equipment at Dolaucothi. The intention was to build a pilot processing plant on the old crushing plant base in the main Open Pit. This would then complete the sequence of events from the mining of gold ore to its processing as a gold bearing concentrate. Subsequently, the concentrate would be treated off site.

An initial design was produced for a building to house this pilot plant with preliminary costs obtained. It was realized at this stage that these costs were beyond the resources available.

Entry portal at Gwynfynydd Gold Mine Dolgellau (c.1999).

Underground ore crushing station at Gwynfynydd Gold Mine (1999).

Shaking table for separation of gold from ore, demonstrated by senior technician, Terry Thomas (1999).

Loading of ore processing equipment at Gwynfynydd Mine in readiness for transport to Dolaucothi (1999).

Gwynfynydd mining and ore processing equipment being received at Dolaucothi (*c.*1999).

Gwynfynydd equipment in receiving bay at Dolaucothi including a large capacity Ingersoll Rand air compressor (*c.*1999).

General view of the mine surface with the old ore crushing plant base as the site for the proposed pilot plant (front left) (*c.*1999).

The 1930s crushing plant base cleared in readiness for the proposed pilot processing plant (*c.*1999).

SUMMARY OF FIELD CENTRE DEVELOPMENT, 1969–1999

A summary of some of the significant stages in the development of the Dolaucothi Field Centre is given below. However, while the twenty-one year period 1978–1999 witnessed the major developments referred to above, the periods from 1970–1978 and from 1999 onwards are relevant in the recent history and continuing story of the Dolaucothi Gold Mine.

1969–1971   First University College Cardiff (UCC) involvement as part of The Dolaucothi Research Committee.

1970–1972   Surveys of Mine workings and gold content in the 1939 Tailing Ponds material by the Department of Mineral Exploitation.

1974–1975   Geological Survey of the mine workings by the Department of Mineral Exploitation (UCC).

1977–1978   Short duration field visits to the mine by mining engineering and mining geology students.

1978   Head Lease of the mine granted to UCC by the Crown Estate Commissioners for the 21-year period, 1978–1999.

1978   Commencement of undergraduate vacation field courses and staff/student summer camps

1979   Trust Fund established with donations from companies and individuals.

1979   Exploration projects in the Cothi Valley by students located new geological anomalies pointing to the presence of gold-bearing rocks.

1979   Surface drill rig donated to UCC by Anglo-Canadian Exploration (ACE) Ltd. Drilling commenced on Allt-y-Brunant located new gold mineralisation.

1980   Portable air compressor and underground rock drilling equipment donated by Atlas Copco (UK) Ltd.

1981   First joint National Trust (NT)/University College Cardiff trial mine visitor exercise.

1983   Completion of Phase One rehabilitation of the lease area of the mine workings. Crown Licence granted to UCC to allow NT to hold sub-lease on the mine for purposes of tourism.

1983   Commencement of National Trust-organised visits by the public on an annual basis from April to September.

1984   Following refurbishment of the drill rig, long term drilling programmes commenced to understand the nature of the gold mineralisation; sponsored by ACE Ltd.

1984   Donation of a range of miscellaneous surface and underground equipment by British Coal, South Wales

1985   Construction of workshop and other surface facilities. First sublease granted by UCC to the NT for the purpose of tourism. Opening of the new NT Visitor Centre.

1986   Donation by Courtaulds PLC of the Olwyn Goch Mine surface buildings and headframe from the Halkyn lead/zinc area of North Wales.

1987/88   Erection of the Olwyn Goch buildings and headframe by the NT at Dolaucothi.

1998   Commencement of negotiations for a new Head Lease to operate the Mine as a Field Centre with the Crown Estates and the NT in a tripartite arrangement.

1998   Anglesey Mining Plc took over the exploration licence around the mine from ACE Ltd and funded further diamond drilling by the Department of Earth Sciences.

1998   Negotiation begun for the transfer of mining and processing plant equipment from the closed Gwynfynydd Gold Mine near Dolgellau, North Wales.

1999   Feasibility studies made for the construction of a surface ore processing pilot plant in conjunction with the development of a tunnel drivage connecting Long and Mill Adits. Transfer of Gwynfynydd equipment to Dolaucothi.

1999   Head Lease transferred to the NT by the Crown Estate Commissioners.

DOLAUCOTHI EDUCATION PROJECT
1989–1992

**THE KING'S HEAD
LLANDEILO
DYFED**

**UNIVERSITY OF WALES
COLLEGES AT
CARDIFF & LAMPETER**

**FACULTY OF EDUCATION
& COMBINED STUDIES
CAERLEON**

VIII

THE DOLAUCOTHI EDUCATION PROJECT
1989–1992

EDUCATION AND THE WIDER WORLD

A major aim of the Department of Mineral Exploitation in the 1970s was the development of a Mining Field Centre at the Dolaucothi Gold Mine to serve the needs of students in higher education. In addition, the longer-term vision also included linking the University with the whole of the education community, the people of Pumsaint and District and the wider world.

Initially, this was achieved naturally by the interaction between staff and students as part of their vacation programmes and their dependence on facilities provided by the people in the locality, such as catering and accommodation. Subsequently, the National Trust employed student guides for the mine tours by the general public.

Apart from the three editions of the publication, *The Dolaucothi Gold Mines, Geology and Mining History*, that described the geology and mining history of the gold mine, there was little other reading material that would be of general interest to the public. University staff felt that visitors, particularly children and their teachers could be helped by the production of educational materials that dealt with the folklore of the area and the Roman period of activity, important subject areas of the National Curriculum for schools (Curriculum Cymreig in Wales).

ESTABLISHMENT OF THE PROJECT

The interest shown in the gold mines site by the visiting public during the years of rehabilitation and development, 1978–1984, stimulated a new education initiative aimed specifically at Primary schools. Informal discussions between the University and the National Trust in 1987 were followed in 1988 by formal proposals that saw the inclusion in the Project of the Gwent College of Higher education (later to become the University of Wales College, Newport). Teacher training at Primary level had been a strong component of the College's programmes for many years.

The differing interests of each of the three parties were merged into a central aim stated as the development of the education potential of the gold mines and the surrounding estate. Approval of the proposals by the authorities of each of the bodies enabled research to commence in April 1989 under a management structure responsible for coordination and momentum of the Project.

With their long experience of Primary education, Gwent College accepted responsibility for the development of new materials such as teachers' resource packs and children's worksheets. This arrangement provided the focus for the Project research work by the College's staff and students. University and National Trust staff assisted this activity particularly in relation to visits to the mine and nearby sites, but also in visits to some of the Primary schools participating in the Project.

PROJECT ORGANISATION AND FINANCE

Overall management of the Project was undertaken by senior representatives of the three partners, namely, Emrys Evans, Land Agent for the National Trust, Dr Anthony Saul, Deputy Principal of Gwent College, and Dr Alun Isaac, Senior Lecturer and Mine Manager on behalf of the University Colleges involved. Their personal interest and enthusiasm for the Project was primarily responsible for its establishment and continuing development.

Following a preliminary meeting of the Management Steering Group in July 1988, and commencing in December 1988, meetings were arranged at a regular two-monthly frequency for the life of the project. The meetings were held on a rotational basis at venues that included Cardiff, Caerleon, Lampeter, Llandeilo and Pumsaint (Dolaucothi).

The Steering Group comprised the above-named together with colleagues from each of the partnering bodies including Charlotte Clough and Helen Jones, National Trust, Margaret Isaac and Dr Raymond Howell, Gwent College, Dr Alwyn Annels, Cardiff and Dr Barry Burnham, Lampeter, of the University of Wales. In addition, the group were joined at several meetings by Molly Rees, Advisory Teacher, Dyfed Education Authority, and Carole Brooks, Head teacher, Lliswerry Junior School, Newport.

Dolaucothi Education Project, Management Steering Group meeting at the National Trust Regional office, The King's Head, Llandeilo (1991).
Left to Right: Dr Raymond Howell, Helen Jones, Susan Lloyd-Fern, John Longworth-Kraft, Margaret Isaac, Dr Anthony Saul.

With the focus of the project centred at Gwent College of Higher Education, Caerleon, organisation of the research was undertaken by members of the academic staff, principally, Margaret Isaac (English Department) and Dr Raymond Howell (History Department). Both members of staff pursued their own disciplines in working towards the production of teachers' resource packs in English and Welsh entitled, *Welsh Legend and Culture* (*Chwedlau a Diwylliant Cymru*), (Isaac, 1991) and *The Romans* (*Y Rhufeiniaid*), (Howell, 1991).

Other members of academic and technical staff of Gwent College were involved with the Project as it proceeded. Being a teacher-training establishment, students were also involved in the research from the start providing valuable enthusiasm and advice in the various student projects that formed part of the overall work.

Appropriate contributions to the finance required for the Project were obtained from each of the three partnering bodies with the organisation of this aspect being undertaken by the National Trust. However, the Trust's expertise and experience of raising funds from a wider circle of interested parties produced significant grant aid from the Countryside Commission for Wales and the Baring Foundation. In total, approximately £50,000 was raised from various sources towards the costs involved in the research and for the publication of the teachers' resource packs.

PROJECT ACTIVITIES

The *Welsh Legend and Culture* study provides an example of the research activities involved in the project. At commencement, three senior students of Gwent College formed part of a team that were led by the staff tutor, Margaret Isaac. Each of the students were given responsibility for developing areas of study that linked with subjects of the National Curriculum, e.g. Mathematics, Science and Geography (Peter Cornelious), Music, Drama and Dance (Sally-Ann Jones), and History, Art and Craft (Ann-Marie Spooner).

In general, teamwork was followed at the College with regular planning and progress meetings. As part of the project, visits were made to Dolaucothi Gold Mine and surrounding areas such as the Rhandirmwyn area and the Llyn Brianne Reservoir. One such visit of great appeal was to the cave on Dinas Rock, on the Royal Society for the Protection of Birds (RSPB) nature reserve, the hiding place of Twm Siôn Cati, the Welsh outlaw of Tudor times. In conjunction with their normal teacher-training, the team established a Case Study school to involve teachers and children in the development of the resource pack and worksheets. Report writing was a feature of this project, providing information for the Resource Materials Pack (Cornelious, 1989).

At the exit from the upper levels of the Dolaucothi Gold Mine. Margaret Isaac with senior year project students of Gwent College (*c.*1988).

Lliswerry Junior School, Newport, was selected as the case study school with the team being joined by the headteacher, Carole Brooks, and the classteacher of the trial class, Alison Jones. The class, comprising 35 children (12 boys and 23 girls) aged 9-10 years, also made visits to the gold mine and the cave. In addition to a regular programme of lessons at the school by the students, talks were also given by a member of the University (Dr Alun Isaac) with video filming of school and visit activities by Roy Manchee of Gwent College.

While the school lessons produced a variety of children's work that reflected their interest and motivation, the educational visits produced a wealth of resource material in the form of cave rubbings, scientific samples, word banks, video film, and photographs. The interest and excitement of the children during the visits to the mine is captured in the photographs that follow.

In Twm Siôn Cati's Cave on Dinas Rock, part of the RSPB Reserve near Llyn Brianne, Carmarthenshire (*c.*1989).

Gwent College staff and students on location at the start of the Dolaucothi Education Project in preparation for the development of the *Welsh Legend and Culture* Resource Materials Pack.

Exciting time for primary
schoolchildren putting on helmets
and caplamps for the visit to the
Mine (*c.*1990).

The traditional group photograph
before the mine tour (*c.*1990).

The National Trust guide, at Middle Adit, explaining how the folded rocks might indicate the presence of gold (*c.*1990).

Great interest with the children making notes on their clipboards when inside the mine (*c.*1990).

Schoolchildren at the mine exit point in Mitchell Pit after their tour in 1991. (Note: Molly Rees, 2nd from right, back row, a Primary Level Adviser to the Project).

Children at school making a model Roman fort as part of their case study in the development of *The Romans* Teaching Resource Materials Pack (1990).

TEACHERS' RESOURCE MATERIALS PACKS

Both teachers' resource materials packs were published by the National Trust in 1991 entitled, *Welsh Legend and Culture* and *The Romans*. For immediate identification by schools, they were referred to as Resource Materials for the National Curriculum with the former, a literature-based topic pack, and the latter, a topic pack based on elements of Roman history.

The literature-based pack, *Welsh Legend and Culture*, comprised a short introduction. This was followed by a Teachers' Guide, a series of five short stories based around the area of the gold mine, classroom activities, site activities and examples of trialling evidence. While the work producing the contents of the pack was essentially from the case study school, similar activity was trialled at two other schools in Dyfed, one through the medium of Welsh at Hendy Primary School, Pontardulais, and the other in English, at Halfway County Primary School, Llanelli. In both cases, the class teachers independently used some of the materials suggested and adapted other elements to pursue their own lines of teaching.

The history-based pack comprised four booklets entitled, *The Romans in South Wales, Teaching the Topic Pack: The Romans, The Romans and the National Curriculum*, and *Roman Gold – An Activity Book*. A series of workcards were also included to complement the booklets. As in the case of the literature-based topic pack, trialling of the materials was pursued at schools in Gwent (Duffryn Junior School) and in Dyfed (Ysgol Gymraeg Brynsierfel, Llwynhendy, Llanelli). Examples of children's work were included in both packs giving an indication of their enjoyment of the activities and the quality of their learning and understanding.

COVERS OF THE *WELSH LEGEND AND CULTURE* TEACHER'S RESOURCE MATERIALS PACK.

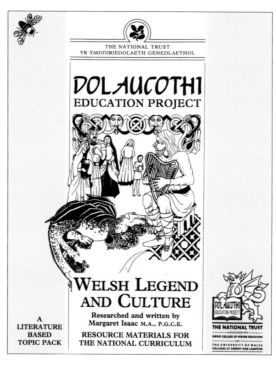

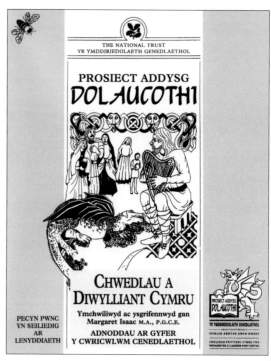

COVERS OF *THE ROMANS* TEACHER'S RESOURCE MATERIALS PACK.

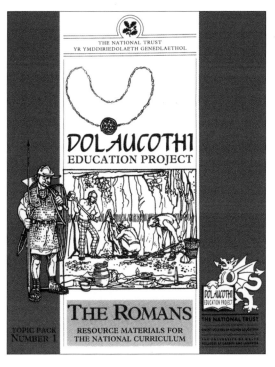

THE OFFICIAL LAUNCH

To bring the results of the three-year programme to the attention of the wider world, particularly schools in Wales, an official launch was planned to take place on 15 October 1991. Previously, on 10 July 1990, an Education Awareness Day had taken place at the mine site involving the trial schools, civic dignitaries and representatives of Dyfed Local Education Authority. This activity had given valuable experience to all involved in the Project.

Prys Edwards, Chairman of the Wales Tourist Board at the time, opened the Official Launch proceedings in a specially erected marquee in the Open Pit of the gold mine. Senior officers of all the partners in the Project were present together with a wide range of Education Authority representatives, teachers from several of the Dyfed schools, teachers and children who had been involved in the research activities, and invited visitors. Media representatives were present to film the launch ceremony and the activities of the schoolchildren of the trial schools.

Copies of the resource packs were purchased at the launch and subsequently by many of those present and encouraging views were expressed about their content and presentation by the teachers present.

Emrys Evans, Land Agent of the National Trust, officially opening the Education Awareness Day in July 1990.

Prys Edwards, Chairman, Wales Tourist Board, speaking at the Official Launch of the Education Project Teachers' Resource Materials Packs for Primary schools in October 1991.

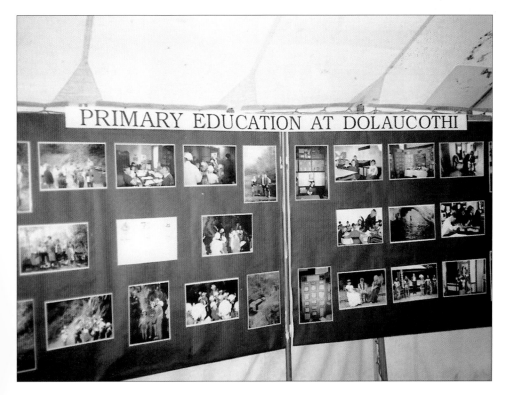

Display of the pilot schools' activities from 1988–1991 at the Official Launch (1991).

Mr Claude Paige of the National Trust viewing the display of University activities in the three year Education project (1991).

Professor Roy Evans, Head of the School of Engineering, Cardiff University (1988–1994), on left, hearing about continuing developments from Dr Alwyn Annels (1991).

DISTRIBUTION AND MARKETING OF THE RESOURCE PACKS

The Management Steering Group continued to meet following the official launch to discuss appropriate ways of marketing the resource materials with sales to libraries and schools in Dyfed, Gwent and other parts of Wales. To complete project activity, the copies remaining after sales had eventually diminished were distributed to all schools in Dyfed.

The long term success of the project to the Gold Mines site may be gauged by the continuing number of visits by schools, and by the subsequent development of the materials at Gwent College. Both topic packs served as lecture and student project material in teacher-training programmes. In addition and in answer to a call by Prys Edwards, at the Official Launch, the lecturers involved continued their research in the chosen topics. Margaret Isaac has continued to write stories on the folklore related to places in Wales and Dr Ray Howell has continued his research with publications on Caerwent and other places of Roman activity in Gwent.

Visits to schools since the Official Launch of the resource materials show that the packs are still in use in English and Welsh medium schools.

National Trust staff and visitors present at the Education Awareness Day.
Left to Right: Charlotte Clough and Helen Jones – Organisers (*c.*1990).

Extract from early publicity material
when visits officially commenced in
1984.

IX

CONSERVATION
AND PUBLIC RELATIONS

THE VISITING PUBLIC

The foregoing sections of this book indicate that one of the primary aims had been largely satisfied in the rehabilitation of Dolaucothi Gold Mine, namely, the development of a Field Centre serving the higher education community.

The combined work of the University and the National Trust during the second and third phases of the project in particular, had simultaneously acted to satisfy a further aim, notably, the conservation of a unique site and the broadening of its technical and general appeal.

As a result of these activities, the third aim of raising public awareness and interest can be seen in the annual number of visitors from 1983 onwards, and the total number of visitors in the period 1983 to 2009, as given below.

Prior to the start of rehabilitation of the main section of the Gold Mine, small numbers of National Trust members had often visited the Dolaucothi Mine site in the period from 1960 onwards with the publication of the ongoing archaeological work by Manchester University.

With the commencement of activity by Mineral Exploitation staff in the 1970s, public interest was raised further. From 1978 onwards, staff and students regularly interacted with the public during the initial rehabilitation work, answering questions such as:

How much gold is in the mine?	*Have you found any gold?*
How did the Romans know about the gold?	*Where did the gold come from?*
Why are University students here?	*Can we look inside? Please?*
Do you have any free samples?	

The start of the mine tour commencing in the Open Pit with the National Trust guide giving the history of the mine and how the gold was mined by the Romans and later miners. Note the compressor house and air receivers in the background and the drillstone (on the right) used as a commemorative symbol of the mine rehabilitation and reopening as a visitor attraction (c.1995).

Many more questions of both a serious and light-hearted nature indicated the general interest and potential tourism benefits of the new development. Being naturally enthusiastic and enterprising, the students enjoyed the interaction with the general public and the rewards that often came their way as a result. However, for legal reasons, they were not permitted to take visitors into the mine.

Recognising the need to satisfy their members' curiosity about the mine workings and wishing to stimulate this interest further, the National Trust organised a series of trial exercises in conjunction with University academic staff from 1981 to 1983. This allowed an assessment to be made of the viability of mine tours. The success of this innovation and its addition to the tourist nature of the region encouraged the National Trust to establish Dolaucothi Gold Mine as a major visitor attraction. Commencing in 1983, visitor numbers from 25,000 to 30,000 were being recorded each year so that by summer 1987, it was clear that there was a demand for the experience of a visit to a goldmine that had been worked by the Romans and others.

Initially, the presence of Cardiff University staff and students engaged on mine rehabilitation work and/or field course education programmes created new public interest at Dolaucothi. This was stimulated further by the erection in 1987 of the Olwyn Goch machinery, especially the shaft headgear and winding engine, and the new buildings. The positive publicity given to the site by the National Trust and the tourism authorities increased the number of visits by Trust members and the wider public.

Of the more than 700,000 visitors to the site since 1983, approximately 50% were members of the National Trust, the remainder being people from the UK and Europe of a very wide range of ages. The relatively uniform number of visitors to the site since 2001 (20,000 to 25,000 per year) shows that adults and children were enjoying the experience of visiting an exciting and interesting regional and national asset. The comments in the Guests Record Book kept at the mine provide evidence of visitor response and some of the current comments are included later in the following section.

Another group of visitors ready for the tour with the workshop/laboratory in the background (*c.*1995).

The visitors leaving the Open Pit for the upper levels of the mine, accompanied by two guides. (Each tour of from 10 to 20 members of the public was attended by one guide leading the group and one at the rear) (*c.*1995).

A party of visitors at the portal of Middle Adit – grandparents, parents and children (*c.*1995).

The leader guide (on left) at the entry to Mitchell Adit, explaining what visitors would see inside the mine and answering questions from those who were curious and a few who were a little apprehensive (1995).

A family group inside the mine with an experienced student guide (*c.*1995).

The lower of the three 1930s settling ponds containing water and fine waste rock particles (tailings) with minute amounts of gold (*c*.1995).

The overflow from the 1930s settling ponds reaching the main Open Pit.

ROMAN MINE WORKINGS OUTSIDE THE LEASE AREA

The evidence of Roman mining activity to the south of the main Open Pit held much interest for University staff and students. Although the University rehabilitation and development activities were confined to the lease area shown and described previously, the trench-shaped open pit and connected underground tunnels were of interest because of their shape and the reason for their existence.

It was thought that the Lower and Upper Roman Adits were excavated by hand because of the many pick marks on the roof and sides and were used to

A family group on a popular activity after the mine tour, 'panning for gold' at the bottom of the stream that flowed down the hillside from the 1930s tailings ponds (*c.*1995).

transport broken ore from the higher level of the trench pit to a more convenient surface transit route. The shape of the Lower Adit was thought to allow miners to carry sacks or baskets of ore on their shoulders, and the square shape of the Upper Adit allowed ore movement using some form of manual or horse-drawn conveyance. Evidence for this lies in the horizontal score marks along the walls of this adit.

View from inside Lower Roman Adit showing the horseshoe profile (*c.*1991).

Pick marks in the roof and sides of Lower and Upper Roman Adits, typical of Roman tunnel excavation techniques.

View looking into Upper Roman Adit showing the square profile (c.1991).

Following the success of the public visitor tours of the main mine workings, the National Trust decided to extend the public tours to the Roman Adits and provide an alternative tour of specifically Roman interest. This has also become a popular choice of the visitors.

Public visitors on a guided tour in Upper Roman Adit (c.1991).

Teachers and education advisers in Upper Roman Adit with Professor Barry Burnham, Archaeology Department, Lampeter (1992).

The group of teachers and advisers in one of the Roman trench type open pits with Professor Burnham describing the layout and method of mining (1992).

During the University activity at Dolaucothi, the National Trust arranged a number of reunions of those mineworkers who had been active in the 1930s period of mining prior to abandonment of the mine in 1940. It was a pleasant way of meeting these gentlemen and hearing the many stories and recollections in the garden of the Dolaucothi Hotel on a warm sunny day.

First Annual Reunion of some of the Dolaucothi mineworkers of the 1930s in the grounds of the Dolaucothi Hotel, Pumsaint (c.1981).

THE NATIONAL TRUST
YR YMDDIRIEDOLAETH GENEDLAETHOL

X

CHANGING TIMES

In 1999, the lease of the mine workings to operate as an engineering field centre and public visitor facility was transferred by the Crown Commissioners to the National Trust. The Trust as Owner of the mine was regarded as the most appropriate leaseholder for the longer term vision of the site, and for the benefit of all involved. This occurred simultaneously with changes at the University involving staff retirements, new education programmes and new policy initiatives.

General view of the site in summer 2010 with visitors at the lamproom (building at rear). The lighter pathway on the floor to the left of the picture has been made smooth for the passage of wheelchairs along the mine surface.
(Courtesy: The National Trust).

From 2000 onwards, archaeological activity at the Dolaucothi Mine was given priority by the National Trust within an overall strategic development philosophy. However, the public visitor initiative continued to develop and on a visit to the site in 2011, a photographic record was made to show some of the changes made by the National Trust to enhance visitor experience when at Dolaucothi on one of the different guided tours now offered.

Entrance to Long Adit showing the floor smoothing for ease of wheelchair access along the length of the adit. The railtrack and ballast originally installed by the University for removal of waste rock, was removed to give added height and easier access for visitors (2010).

View of the inbye end of Long Adit immediately beyond the internal shaft showing some lengths of the former railtrack left in place (2010).

At the bottom of the internal shaft in Long Adit showing the base of a new steel ladderway (2010).

Looking down the internal shaft from the top of the ladderway in Mitchell Adit. The steel ladderway and platforms were installed to replace the previous wooden structure. Public visits do not include climbing through the shaft as part of the tour (2010).

Improved surface walkway arrangements provided for travel between the lower and upper levels of the mine (2010).

An improved system provided for the 'panning for gold' activity that has proved popular with adults and children alike (2010).

The interior of the mechanical engineering workshop with a display of equipment typical of that used in the 1930s; note the overhauled and repainted electric battery locomotive on the left (2010).

Recent clearing of an area above the mine site reveals the foundations of the 1930s miners' barracks and a small washhouse (2010).

Sandra Parry, a former chief guide at the mine pointing out the surface features of one of the trench-type surface mines at Dolaucothi (2010).

New safety provision at the exit from the Upper Roman Adit when emerging out into the surface mine. Note a wooden wheel constructed by National Trust staff for the movement of water in certain situations, in this case, previously used at the gold panning site in the main Open Pit (c.2010).

Extended cover and facilities provided for tearoom users when requiring shelter from shade or rain (2010).

ARGORWYD YR ADEILAD HWN YN SWYDDOGOL AR 19eg EBRILL 1991 AR ACHLYSUR ADUNIAD MWYNGLODDWYR Y TRIDEGAU

THIS BUILDING WAS OFFICIALLY OPENED ON THE 19th OF APRIL 1991 AT THE REUNION OF THE 1930's MINE WORKERS

Plaque erected to commemorate opening of the tearoom in 1991 and a reunion of some of the miners of the 1930s (2010).

A measure of the current visitor response to the development of the tours of the mines can be gauged from the comments placed in the Guests Record Book held at Dolaucothi. A sample of these comments for 2010 supplied by National Trust staff is given below.

Very interesting – great day out.

Really informative and clear – Very interesting.

Lovely day out – very interesting tour – great tour guide.

Great tour – thanks – fascinating experience.

Loved gold panning – very interesting and enjoyable.

Splendid informative Victorian and Roman tours, very friendly and knowledgeable staff – Much enjoyed.

Very educational – excellent guided tour and well worth the visit.

Great place! Underground tour was very good.

Very, very, very golden place.

I loved gold panning – great and interesting experience.

XI

VISION AND THE FUTURE

VISIONS

The uniqueness, beauty, and utilitarian qualities of gold have been recognised by world cultures for thousands of years. Welsh gold inspired ancient metal smiths to create ingenious weapons and resplendent jewellery. Roman generals seized on Welsh gold to enable them to perpetuate their role throughout their known world. Gold at Dolaucothi continued to be produced for a short period in the 1930s before the mine became deserted and derelict.

Changing circumstances, necessities, and coincidences brought about perhaps the most ambitious and visionary series of activities in the gold mine in recent times. The necessity of the Department of Mineral Exploitation to seek a new field centre; renewed archaeological activity in the 1970s and 1980s; changing demands of the world mining industries to extend teaching programmes to cover all areas of metals and minerals; all this required the vision of the University at Cardiff to see and seize on the opportunity to create a field centre suitable for academic and practical instruction in all areas of the mining and minerals curriculum: the vision was born.

The rehabilitation of part of the underground workings of the Dolaucothi Gold Mines complex began in 1978. Under existing Mines and Quarries legislation, this part of the complex had been declared officially abandoned in 1940, and shortly afterwards, it became the property of the National Trust following donation of the Dolaucothi Estate by the last surviving member of the Lloyd-Johnes family.

Initially, the University vision was primarily concerned with establishing a site effectively under its control, but in conjunction with the requirements of the National Trust and the Crown Estate Commission. However, during the early years of activity at the site, the interest of National Trust members and the public encouraged a broader view of that vision to include public awareness. The wider and growing interest in conservation, industrial archaeology, tourism and employment prospects encouraged further investment and sponsorship so that Dolaucothi offered an on-going contribution to the region and to posterity.

Several significant changes occurred during the twenty-one year period of the University lease of the gold mine site, in particular, the merging of the two University colleges in Cardiff in 1987, the formation of the School of Engineering in 1988, and the ending of mining education at Cardiff in 1991/92. Enriched by access to extended expertise as a result of the colleges merging, work continued in realising the broader vision for Dolaucothi. Subsequently, the combined efforts of the University and the National Trust encouraged and enabled opportunities for achievement of the potential outcomes of the venture.

It would be true to say that a number of aims referred to previously in this account of the Dolaucothi project did not come to fruition. This was due to the changes referred to immediately above and to technical and financial constraints. These aims included:

- The Long Adit to Mill Adit tunnel drivage that did not progress beyond the early stage of junction formation;

- The construction of a pilot processing plant using the equipment brought down from the closed Gwynfynydd Mine, Dolgellau;

- Establishing access to parts of the underground section of the mine below the Open Pit;

- Completion of geological studies, that included the drilling programme, and the production of a definitive geological report and/or scientific paper.

However, accepting that the 21-year period of lease held by the University required a realistic approach to what was possible in that timescale, the overall success of the project may be gauged by the outcomes referred to below.

OUTCOMES

University Education
The estimated number of undergraduate and postgraduate students involved in the early studies, and the rehabilitation and development activities covering the period from 1970 to 1999 is 2,500–3,000. Each of these men and women

benefited from their contact with an industrial setting; from the social contact between themselves and their staff tutors, and the contrast between the academic environment of the University precincts and the world of work. Many of these students have established successful careers in a range of engineering and other activities. They recognised the satisfaction and the enjoyment in their achievement at that time and acknowledged the quality of learning that has assisted their ultimate goals (see Appendix A6).

Primary Education

The excitement of the children involved in the Dolaucothi Education Project was reward in itself for the teachers and parents who accompanied them on their visits to Dolaucothi. The organised visits provided a range of knowledge and ideas across all areas of the curriculum with continuing education activities that extended well beyond the initial visits. The production of teaching resources relevant to the curriculum in Wales enabled schools to use them year by year and build upon them with the new teaching approaches being introduced. A conservative estimate of the number of children involved in the Dolaucothi project lies between 1,000 and 1,500.

Conservation

The University and the National Trust worked closely together pursuing common goals, i.e. continuing education and conservation. The strength of these combined forces resulted in the acquisition of new materials and equipment which increased the quality and appearance of the goldmine as a University field centre, a focus for learning and a model of conservation. The project prospered and public interest increased.

Following completion of the rehabilitation programme from 1978 to 1983/84, the National Trust was successful in 1986/87 in organising the major upgrading of the Dolaucothi site. The introduction of the virtually complete 1930s vintage mine surface buildings and equipment from North Wales changed the appearance of the mine and had a great impact upon all those involved at the mine. The addition of support buildings for visitors such as, a visitor centre, helmets and lamps facility and tearoom services, and a gift shop provided a welcoming environment.

There is little doubt that without the positive action of the National Trust in undertaking the responsibility for the long term care and maintenance of the Olwyn Goch Mine equipment, it could have been acquired by other more commercially-minded operators, or allowed to deteriorate and eventually be scrapped. Instead, the benefits resulting from the collaboration of the National Trust and University include: the field of industrial archaeology, lifelong learning, tourism and conservation.

The philosophy of the National Trust in displaying the mine surface equipment in working order and using it can be regarded as a conservation strategy that links well with the successful present-day variety of approaches being introduced at other regional museums such as at Aberdulais Falls and Newton House, Dinefwr.

Employment

From 1970–1999 many local people were employed during the rehabilitation of the goldmine. The warm and enthusiastic support of the people of Pumsaint and District ensured that the University staff and students operated effectively while at work. Accommodation and catering at a variety of homes in surrounding villages provided welcome employment in a rural area. The tearoom facility also required staffing during field courses that took place in out-of-season periods. Their dedication and enthusiasm demonstrated interest and commitment to their own history and culture.

The visitor season, March to October, offered further employment opportunities for guides on the mine tours, and for staff in the visitor centre, the tearoom and the gift shop. From 13 to 17 persons are now employed at the site each day, depending on the time in the visitor season. On occasions, there could also be on site, consultancy staff, members of the National Trust's Buildings and Estate team, and the Property Manager. More widely, further employment results from increased numbers of tourists and visitors to the local area.

Tourism

The forecast number of visitors to the site as a consequence of the upgrading of the site in 1987/88 was from 20,000 to 30,000 per year. The best estimate of the total number of visitors to the site since 1983 is 700,000, this number being based on information supplied by National Trust staff for the years 2000 to 2008, and information supplied in previous years. The average annual number at present is approximately 25,000.

The financial effect of the visitor charges enables the site to be largely self-sustaining. The gift shop provides opportunities for further income; this activity operates separately, under National Trust Enterprises.

The Dolaucothi Gold Mines include the workings of the Romans and the 1930s. The National Trust recognised this further potential for visitor interest and recently introduced a range of alternative tours of the mines' complex, such as the Victorian Tour and the Roman Tour aimed at raising the attractiveness of a visit to the site, thereby increasing visitor numbers and income. The additional opportunity for visitors to 'pan for gold' in the nearby stream that leads down from the old waste tailings ponds is an added attraction.

Carmarthenshire is a county with numerous visitor attractions and Dolaucothi sits well in the regional picture. Attractive brochures describing a day at the gold mine are in evidence at most of the tourist venues and many hotels. The Carmarthenshire Antiquarian Society also provided assistance for the archaeological research of the Roman mining period by Manchester University in the 1960s/1970s.

THE VISION FOR THE FUTURE

Gold has many connotations. It has produced wealth, beauty, science, and engineering. It has enabled doctors to heal and men to explore space. It has also engendered tyranny and greed. Gold has created and destroyed empires and civilisations and has fed the imagination of poets and artists.

The rehabilitation and development of the Dolaucothi Gold Mine was brought to fruition by vision, imagination, initiative, opportunity and resources. It also required the dedication, hard work and commitment of many people. It is hoped that such golden opportunities will continue to be exploited and developed by future generations.

Continuing such an enterprise is a challenge.

The realisation of the vision enshrined in this book is given substance by the outcomes referred to above. This illustrated account pays tribute to the many people at Cardiff University and the National Trust who participated in an engineering project, unique in the annals of both bodies, and it places on record their contribution to posterity.

APPENDIX

A1: Personnel Involved in the Rehabilitation of
Dolaucothi Gold Mine, 1978-1999

A2: Plans and Photographic Images Associated with the
Dolaucothi Gold Mine Project, 1978-1999/2000

A3: Sponsors of the Dolaucothi Gold Mine Project, 1978-1999

A4: Short Vacation Field Course Activities Schedules
for 1986 and 1987

A5: Extract from an Equipment Inventory of a
1930s Lead/Zinc Mine

A6: Representative Student Groups involved in the
Dolaucothi Gold Mine Project

APPENDIX A1

PERSONNEL INVOLVED IN THE REHABILITATION OF DOLAUCOTHI GOLD MINE, 1978-1999

Cardiff University

Academic Staff

Annels, Alwyn
Brabham, Peter
Brown, Kenneth
Dominy, Simon
Evans, Roy
Hellewell, Edward
Isaac, Alun
Kingston, Gordon
Millman, Anthony
Morgan, Vernon
Platt, John
Pritchard, Hazel
Pooley, Frederick
Rickard, David
Rigby, Neal
Smart, Brian
Steed, Geoffrey
Williams, Keith

Technical Staff

Bevan, David
Castle, Wayne
Davies, Alan
Fisher, Peter
Glinn, David
Hooper, Brian

Jones, Ryland
Morgan, Don
Rowlands, Jeffrey
Webber, Graham

Postgraduate Research Students

Arthur, John
Bradbury, Toby
Cain, Peter
Chanda, William
Cooke, Patrick
Cornes, Stewart
Davies, John
Dey, Matthew
Follington, Ian
Freeman, Paul
Ingram, Simon
Kawecki, Maciej
Kell, Terence
Lloyd, Philip
Neve, Patrick
O'Grady, Paul
Price, Michael
Raffield, Martin
Seymour, Clive
Smallbone, Paul
Thornton, Julian
Thomas, Jonathan

Undergraduate Students

Special acknowledgement is made to the undergraduate students of the School of Engineering and the School of Earth, Ocean and Planetary Sciences, whose efforts contributed to the successful completion of the Dolaucothi project.

THE NATIONAL TRUST
YR YMDDIRIEDOLAETH GENEDLAETHOL

NATIONAL TRUST

Land Agents
Broomhead, Peter
Churchill, Gary
Evans, Emrys
Griffith, Hugh
James, Philip
Longworth-Kraft, John
Mitchell, Peter

Other Staff
Branch, Jean
Clough, Charlotte
Evans, Margaret
Jenkins, Carl
Jones, Helen
Madsen, Annette
Mellor, Alison
Parry, Brian
Parry, Sandra
Plunkett-Dillon, Emma

GWENT COLLEGE OF
HIGHER EDUCATION

UNIVERSITY OF WALES,
LAMPETER

Academic staff

Farr, Michael

Howell, Raymond

Isaac, Margaret

Lawton, Jill

Manchee, Roy

Pugh, Brian

Saul, Anthony

  with

Local Education Authority

  Staff including:

Brooks, Carole, Newport

Jones, Alison, Newport

Rees, Molly, Carmarthenshire

Undergraduate Students

Cornelious, Peter

Jones, Sally-Ann

Spooner, Ann-Marie

Burnham, Barry

Burnham, Helen

  with

Staff at the Dyfed Archaeological

  Trust including:

Benson, Don

Murphy, Ken

Undergraduate Students

Special acknowledgement is made to
the undergraduate students of the
Department of Archaeology,
Lampeter, whose efforts contributed
further knowledge to the Roman
period of mining at Dolaucothi.

The Author wishes to apologise to any former colleagues and students of Cardiff
University, The National Trust, University of Wales, Lampeter, and Gwent
College of Higher Education whose names have been inadvertently omitted
from the above lists.

Plans and Photographic Images Associated with the Dolaucothi Gold Mine Project, 1978-1999/2010

Plans: Dolaucothi Map Repository

(Contact: Dr Peter Brabham, School of Earth, Ocean and Planetary Sciences, Cardiff University)

Photographic Albums

(Contact: Dr Alun Isaac, Formerly, School of Engineering, Cardiff University)

No. 1 Ogofau Gold Mine, 1978-1985 (Mining Field Centre, Department of Mineral Exploitation, University College Cardiff)

No. 2 Ogofau Gold Mine, 1985-1990 (Mining field Centre, Institute of Materials University College Cardiff)

No. 3 Ogofau Gold Mine, 1990-1995 (Dolaucothi Field Centre, School of Engineering University of Wales College Cardiff)

No. 4 Dolaucothi Education Project, 1989-1992 (Dolaucothi Field Centre, Dyfed)

Photographic Slides

No. 1 Personal holding 1975-1999; 2010), Dr Alun Isaac

No. 2 Personal holding (1987-2002), Dr Peter Brabham

Computer Files

No. 1   Personal holding, Dr Alun Isaac

Folder, Alun-Pictures

Sub-folder: Dolaucothi Ref. No. 2010-06-21
AEA Slides
AKI Scans 2010
AKI Slides 2000
Archive images
Book Drawings
Colour diagrams
PJB Drilling Images
PJB FLIKR Website Images
PJB Mine Images

No. 2   Personal holding, Dr Alun Isaac

Digital Scans of Dolaucothi Images (Dr Peter Brabham 2010)

APPENDIX A3

Sponsors of the Dolaucothi Gold mine Project

1. Department of Mineral Exploitation, University College Cardiff

Aber Resources Ltd, Vancouver
Anglesey Mining plc
Anglo-Canadian (ACE) Ltd, Toronto
Atlas Copco (GB) Ltd, UK
The Board of Celtic Studies
Cadw: Welsh Historic Monuments
Consolidated Goldfields Plc, London
The National Coal Board, UK
BP Minerals Ltd
The National Trust
University of Wales College, Cardiff
University of Wales College, Lampeter
Zambia Consolidated Copper Mines Ltd (ZCCM)
Ryan International Ltd., Cardiff
Quest Exploration Ltd.
Golder Associates, Vancouver
Highwood Resources, Calgary
RioTinto Zinc (RTZ) Ltd., London
Carmarthenshire Antiquarian Society
Society of Antiquaries of London
Pantyfedwen Fund
Minerals Industry Careers Unit (MIMCU), London
G. Williams, Consultant
C. R. Ford & I. T. Rozier, Graduates of UCC

2. The National Trust

Courtaulds Viscose Europe
Manpower Services Commission
Science Museum (Fund for the Preservation of Technological
and Scientific Materials)
University of Wales
Various private sponsors
Wales Tourist Board
Welsh Development Agency
Baring Foundation (Dolaucothi Education Project)
Countryside Commission for Wales (Dol. Ed. Project)

APPENDIX A4.1

SHORT VACATION FIELD COURSE ACTIVITIES SCHEDULE FOR 1986

UNIVERSITY COLLEGE CARDIFF
INSTITUTE OF MATERIALS

DEPARTMENT OF MINING, GEOLOGICAL AND MINERALS ENGINEERING
PART 1 MINING ENGINEERING/PART 2 MINING GEOLOGY FIELD COURSE
MINING FIELD CENTRE : 12-19 DECEMBER 1986

Day/Date/Time	A	B	C	D	E	F
			Student Group			
Fri. 12th Dec. 20.00 hr	Travel to Mining Field Centre E.T.D. 14.30 hr/E.T.A. 17.30 hr					
20.00 hr	Mining Engineering Lecture (Visitor Reception Centre)					
Sat. 13th Dec. 09.00 hr	Mining Geology Tour					
	(1) Tunnel Drivage	(5) Geotechnics	(2) Ventilation	(7) Dia.Drilling	(6) Geophysics	(8) Geotechnics
20.00 hr	Mining Geology Lecture/Seminar (Visitor Reception Centre)					
Sun. 14th Dec. 09.00 hr	Geotechnical Lecture					
	(1) Tunnel Drivage	(2) Ventilation	(4) Drainage	(7) Dia.Drilling)	(6) Geophysics	(8) Geotechnics Min. Engineering
Mon. 15th Dec. 09.00 hr	Geotechnical Lecture (Visitor Reception Centre)					
	(2) Ventilation	(1) Tunnel Drivage	(5) Geotechnics	(8) Geotechnics	(7) Dia.Drilling	(6) Geophysics
Tues. 16th Dec.	(4) Drainage	(1) Tunnel Drivage	(3) Minerals Eng.	(8) Geotechnics Min.Engineering	(7) Dia.Drilling	(6) Geophysics
Wed. 17th Dec.	(5) Geotechnics	(3) Minerals Eng.	(1) Tunnel Drivage	(6) Geophysics	(8) Geotechnics	(7) Dia.Drilling
20.00 hr	Minerals Engineering Lecture (Visitor Reception Centre)					
Thurs.18th Dec.	(3) Minerals Eng.	(4) Drainage	(1) Tunnel Drivage	(6) Geophysics	(8) Geotechnics Min.Engineering	(7) Dia.Drilling
Fri. 19th Dec.	Travel to Cardiff E.T.D. 11.30 hr/E.T.A. 13.30.hr.					

APPENDIX A4.2

SHORT VACATION FIELD COURSE ACTIVITIES SCHEDULE 1987

UNIVERSITY COLLEGE CARDIFF

PART 1 MINING & MINERALS ENGINEERING/

PART 2 MINING GEOLOGY FIELD COURSE

MINING FIELD CENTRE : 11-18 DECEMBER 1987

Day/Date/Time	A	B	C	D	E	F
Fri. 11th Dec.	Travel to Mining Field Centre E.T.D. 14.30 hr/E.T.A. 17.30 hr					
20.00 hr	Mining Engineering Lecture (Visitor Reception Centre) (AKI)					
09.00 hr	Mining Geology Tour (AEA/PF/ILF/JD)					
Sat. 12th Dec.	Mine Development (AKI/PNF)	Geotechnics (ILF)	Surface Drilling (Surveying) (AEA/POG)	Surface Drilling (Surveying) (AEA)	Geophysics (PF)	Underground Mapping (JD)
20.00 hr	Mining Geology Lecture/Seminar (Visitor Reception Centre) (AEA)					
Sun. 13th Dec.	Mine Development (AKI/PNF)	Surface Drilling (Surveying) (AEA)	Surveying (POG)	Core Logging (AEA)	Geophysics (PF)	Underground Mapping (JD/ILF)
09.00 hr	Surface Drilling (Surveying) (AEA/POG)	Mine Development (AKI/PNF)	Geotechnics (ILF)	Underground Mapping (JD)	Surface Drilling (Surveying) (AEA)	Geophysics (PF)
Mon. 14th Dec. 20.00 hr	Minerals Engineering Lecture (Visitor Reception Centre) (KPW)					
Tues. 15th Dec.	Surveying (POG)	Mine Development (AKI/PNF)	Minerals Eng. (KPW)	Underground Mapping (JD/ILF)	Core Logging (AEA)	Geophysics (PF)
Wed. 16th Dec.	Geotechnics (AEA)	Minerals Eng. (KPW)	Mine Development (AKI/PNF)	Geophysics (PF)	U/ground Mapping (AEA/JD) U/ground Drilling (ILF/JD)	U/ground Drilling (ILF/JD) Surface Drilling (AEA/POG)
Thurs. 17th Dec.	Minerals Eng. (KPW)	Surveying (POG)	Mine Development (AKI/PNF)	U/ground Drilling (ILF/JD) Geophysics (PF)	U/ground Mapping (JD)	Core Logging (AEA)
Fri. 18th Dec.	Travel to Cardiff E.T.D. 11.30 hr/E.T.A. 13.30 hr.					

Student Group

APPENDIX A4.3

SHORT VACATION FIELD COURSE ACTIVITIES SCHEDULE 1987

UNIVERSITY COLLEGE CARDIFF

INSTITUTE OF MATERIALS

DEPARTMENT OF MINING, GEOLOGICAL AND MINERALS ENGINEERING

PART 2 MINING ENGINEERING FIELD COURSE

MINING FIELD CENTRE : 27 MARCH – 3 APRIL 1987

Day/Date/Time		STUDENT GROUP		
		A	B	C
Fri. 27th Mar.		Travel to Mining Field Centre E.T.A. 18.00 hr		
Sat. 28th Mar.	09.00 hr	Mining Engineering Lectures (Visitor Reception Centre)		
	14.00 hr	Field Visit – Geology/Civil Engineering/Hydrogeology		
Sun. 28th Mar.	09.00 hr 14.00 hr	Geotechnics	Tunnel Drivage	Ventilation/Drainage
Mon. 30th Mar.	09.00 hr 14.00 hr	Survey/Curve Design	Geotechnics	Tunnel Drivage
Tues. 31st Mar.	09.00 hr 14.00 hr	Ventilation/Drainage	Survey/Curve Design	Geotechnics
Wed. 1st Apr.	09.00 hr 14.00 hr	Tunnel Drivage	Ventilation/Drainage	Survey/Curve Design
Thurs. 2nd Apr.	09.00 hr 14.00 hr	Link Tunnel Controls	Mining Operations Tunnel Controls	Mining Operations Tunnel Controls
Fri. 3rd Apr.		Travel to Cardiff E.T.D. 11.30 hr/E.T.A. 13.30 hr		

APPENDIX A5

EXTRACT FROM AN EQUIPMENT INVENTORY OF A 1930S LEAD/ZINC MINE

<u>Area around Headgear</u>

Quantity (where relevant)	Description	Photo no.
	Enamel sign concerning explosives fixed on tree near explosives magazine	3
	Headgear, frame and winding cable	1, 2, 21, 24
100 yds	Railway track, 2 ft gauge, straight and curved rails in situ	10, 11, 12
	Wooden sleepers (elm) 36" x 8" x 3" in situ	12
	Rail dog spikes (2 pairs per sleeper) in situ	10
	Fish plates in situ plus loose ones around tip area	10
	Points lever in situ close to headgear	22
3 sets	Left hand points in situ	
2 sets	Right hand points in situ plus 2 further sets already lifted	11
14	Tubs (Robert Hudson, Leeds) complete and in working order	7, 14, 15
44	Tubs, incomplete. Used as coal bunker, water tank and oil drum support!	5, 9, 23
4	Timber frames for tubs, complete with iron buffers	
	Tippler (incomplete)	8
	Wooden hand-made sawing horse	23
	Banksman's hut, wood and corrugated iron painted green. Contains:	16, 17, 20
	Oil can (watering can)	
	Oil bucket	
	Hand tools including picks, wedge and rubber handled holder, rock drills	18

Winding Engine House

Quantity (where relevant)	Description	Photo no.
	Hoist with twin winding drum. M B Wild and Co Ltd Birmingham. Winding speed indicator in glass case, calibrated in ft/sec.	27, 28, 30, 31, 34, 35, 109, 113
2	Shaft signal equipment panels with bells (now obselete and one much more complete than other)	32
	Code of shaft signals, framed for hanging	39
	Electricity in Mines notice	
	Electricity shock treatment notice	
	Later shaft signal equipment with bell and indicator box marked bottom, adit and top.	
	Cast-iron heating stove and chimney	36
2	Wooden benches, handmade	36
	Wooden hoist operator's cabin, raised up on plinth. Complete with cushions and notices	27
	Brookhirst switchgear	
	Framed drawing (electrical) of Halkyn winder	
2	Fire buckets	38
	Set of spanners	37
	Spare electric motor for winder (on bogie)	38
	Wooden cupboard with double doors. Contents odds and ends	38
	Wooden 4 legged stool	

The above extract is taken from an Inventory of Equipment at the Holywell/Halkyn Mining and Tunnel Company's Olwyn Goch Mine, Rhydymwyn, Clwyd.

REPRESENTATIVE STUDENT GROUPS INVOLVED IN THE DOLAUCOTHI GOLD MINE PROJECT

Mining Engineering undergraduate group (BEng degree) with Dr Neal Rigby on front row left (*c*.1988).

Some of the above group with academic staff at their graduation (*c*.1989).

Exploration Geology undergraduate
student group (BSc degree) with
Dr Peter Brabham on left and
Dr Geoffrey Steed on right (*c*.1994).

Civil Engineering undergraduate
student group (MEng degree) in
happy mood at the beginning of
their week at Dolaucothi (*c*.1998).

SELECT BIBLIOGRAPHY

Annels, A. E. and Burnham, B. C., 1995: *The Dolaucothi Gold Mines: Geology and Mining History* (3rd edition), University of Wales, Cardiff.

Annels. A. E. and Roberts, D. E., 1989: 'Turbidite-hosted gold mineralization at the Dolaucothi Gold Mines, Dyfed, Wales', *Economic Geology*, Vol. 84, 1293-1314.

Benson, Sharon, 1999: 'Geotechnical Design: Link Drivage Study'. Unpublished Project Report, M.Eng. degree in Civil Engineering, Cardiff.

Burnham, Barry and Helen, 2005: *Dolaucothi–Pumsaint: Survey and excavations at a Roman gold-mining complex, 1987-1999*, Oxbow Books, Oxford.

Chrimes, S. B., 1983: *University College Cardiff: A Centenary History 1883-1983*, University of Wales Press, Cardiff.

Cornelious, P. J., 1989: 'IT-INSET Project The Dolaucothi Gold Mines Educational Project, Report No. 1'. Unpublished Project Report, B.Ed. Degree, Gwent College of Higher Education, Caerleon.

Crossley, D. M., 1988: 'The Equipping Phase at the Mining Field Centre, Ogofau Gold Mine'. Unpublished Project Report, B.Eng. degree in Mining Engineering, Cardiff.

Herbert, A. T., 1986: 'A Report on the Holywell/Halkyn Mining and Tunnel Co. Equipment at Rhydymwyn, Clwyd, and its re-use by the National Trust at Dolaucothi, Dyfed'. Unpublished report in the National Trust Records Office, Llandeilo.

Herbert, A. T., 1986: 'Olwyn Goch Mine, Rhydymwyn, Clwyd: Inventory of Equipment'. Unpublished report in the National Trust Records Office, Llandeilo.

Howells, Raymond, 1991: *Dolaucothi Education Project: The Romans.* A History-Based Topic Pack, The National Trust, Llandeilo.

Isaac, M. R., 1991: *Dolaucothi Education Project: Welsh Legend and Culture.* A Literature-Based Topic Pack, The National Trust, Llandeilo.

Jones, G. D. B. and Lewis, P. R., 1971: *The Roman Gold Mines at Dolaucothi,* Carmarthenshire County Council.

Lewis, P. R., 1977: 'The Ogofau Roman Gold Mines at Dolaucothi', *National Trust Yearbook, 1976-77.*

Nelson, T. R. H., 1944: 'Gold Mining in South Wales', *Mine and Quarry Engineering,* 9 January, February, March, issues.

Williams, R., 1970: 'Ogofau Gold Mine'. Unpublished Honours Thesis, B.Eng. degree in Mining Engineering, Cardiff.